ORIGO
STEPPING STONES

2.0

COMPREHENSIVE MATHEMATICS

AUTHORS

James Burnett
Calvin Irons
Peter Stowasser
Allan Turton

PROGRAM CONSULTANTS

Diana Lambdin
Frank Lester, Jr.
Kit Norris

CONTRIBUTING WRITER

Beth Lewis

STUDENT BOOK A

ORIGO
EDUCATION

INTRODUCTION

ORIGO STEPPING STONES 2.0 STUDENT JOURNAL

ORIGO Stepping Stones 2.0 is a world-class comprehensive program, developed by a team of experts to provide a balanced approach to teach and learn mathematics. The Student Journal consists of two parts — Book A and Book B. Book A comprises Modules 1 to 6, and Book B Modules 7 to 12. Each book has Lesson and Practice pages, a complete Contents, Student Glossary, and Teacher Index.

LESSON PAGES

There are two pages for each of the 12 lessons in every module. This sample shows the key components.

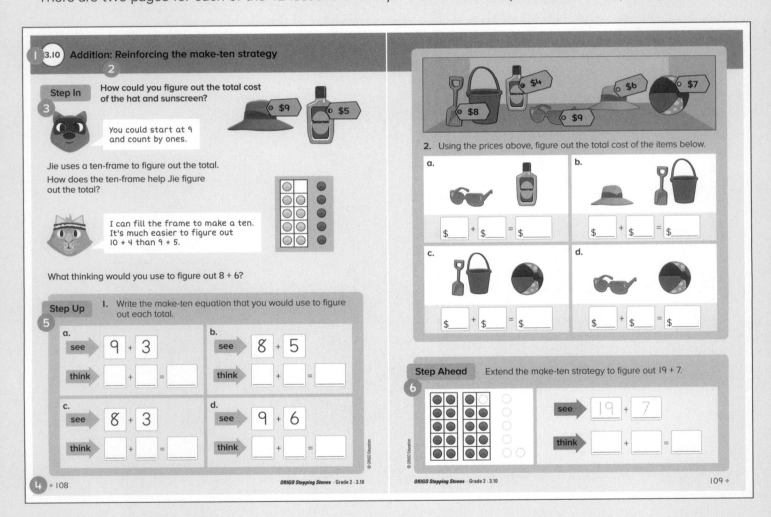

1. Module number and Lesson number.

2. The lesson title tells the content of the lesson. It has two parts: the stem (or big idea), and the leaf (which gives more details).

3. The Step In is designed to generate classroom discourse. Open questions are used to make students think about many methods or answers.

4. For Grade 2, Book A shows a teal diamond beside each page number and index references are in teal. Book B shows a purple diamond and index references are in purple.

5. Step Up provides appropriate written work for the student.

6. The Step Ahead puts a twist on each lesson to develop higher order thinking skills.

PRACTICE PAGES

Lessons 2, 4, 6, 8, 10, and 12 each provide two pages for maintaining concepts and skills. These samples show the key components.

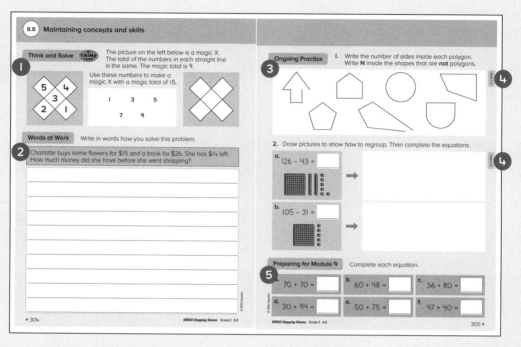

1. The *ORIGO Think Tanks* are a popular way for students to practice problem solving. There are three Think Tank problems in each module.

2. The development of written language is essential. These activities aim to help students develop their academic vocabulary, and provide opportunities for students to write their thinking.

3. Ongoing Practice revisits content previously learned. Question 1 always revisits content from a previous module, and Question 2 revisits content from the current module.

4. This tab shows the originating lesson.

5. Each right-hand page provides content that prepares students for the next module.

6. Regular written practice of mental strategies is essential. There are three computation practice pages that focus on specific strategies in each module.

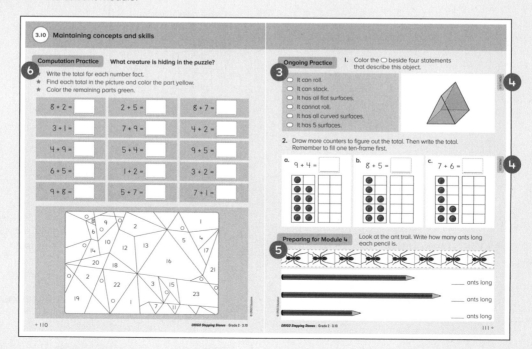

CONTENTS

ORIGO Stepping Stones • Grade 2

CONTENTS

© ORIGO Education

ORIGO Stepping Stones • Grade 2

Step In Look at these number names.

 seventy-two    seventeen   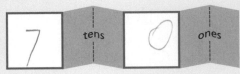 seventy

How would you show the numbers on these expanders?

| 7 | tens | 2 | ones | 1 | tens | 7 | ones | 7 | tens | 0 | ones |

What do you notice when you read and say these numbers?

Do you always say the number of tens first?

Teen comes from the word ten, so seven**teen** means ten and seven more.

What are some other numbers where you say the number of ones first?

What are some other numbers where you say the number of tens first?

Step Up

1. Read the number name.
   Write the number with and without the expander.

a. sixty-three

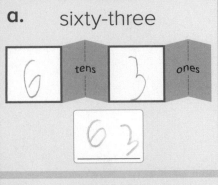
| 6 | tens | 3 | ones |

6 3

b. eighty-four

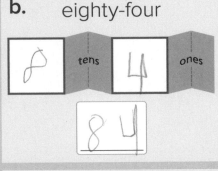
| 8 | tens | 4 | ones |

8 4

c. ninety-two

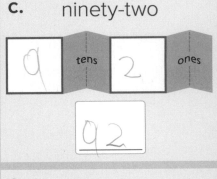
| 9 | tens | 2 | ones |

9 2

d. fifty-six

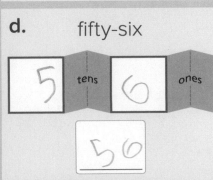
| 5 | tens | 6 | ones |

5 6

e. twenty-eight

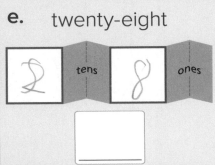
| 2 | tens | 8 | ones |

f. thirty-two

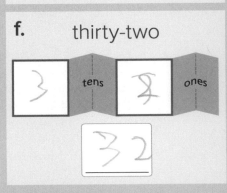
| 3 | tens | 2 | ones |

3 2

2. Write the number with and without the expander.

a. seventy-one

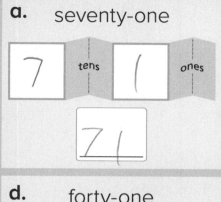

| 7 tens | 1 ones |

71

b. nineteen

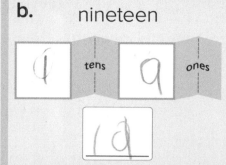

| 1 tens | 9 ones |

19

c. seventy-four

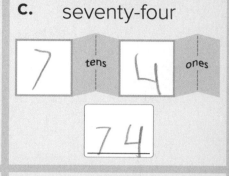

| 7 tens | 4 ones |

74

d. forty-one

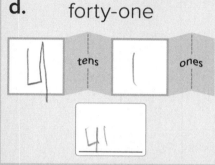

| 4 tens | 1 ones |

41

e. forty

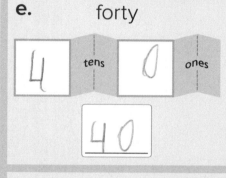

| 4 tens | 0 ones |

40

f. fourteen

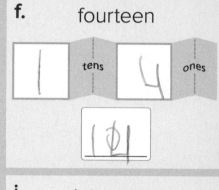

| 1 tens | 4 ones |

14

g. sixteen

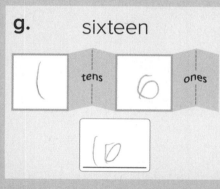

| 1 tens | 6 ones |

16

h. sixty

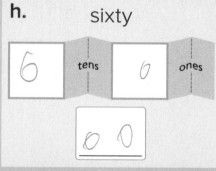

| 6 tens | 0 ones |

00

i. sixty-seven

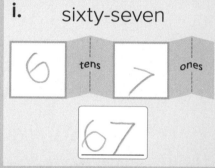

| 6 tens | 7 ones |

67

Step Ahead Read the clues. Write the number on the expander to match.

a.

I am greater than 60 and less than 70.
You say my number when you start at 5
and count by fives.

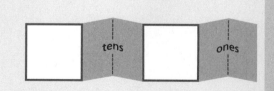

b.

I am less than 50 and greater than 30.
You say my number when you start at 10
and count by tens.

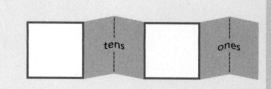

Step In Look at the number on this expander.

How do you read and say the number?

Color blocks to show the same number.

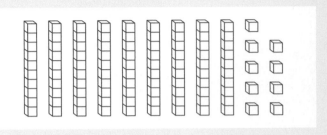

How many people would be needed
to show the number with their fingers?

How would you write the number without using the expander?

How would you write the number name? fifty-

Step Up **1.** Write the number of tens and ones on the expander.
Then write the numeral and number name.

a.

tens   ones   45

forty-

b.

tens   ones

twenty-

c.

tens   ones

2. Complete these mix-and-match puzzles.

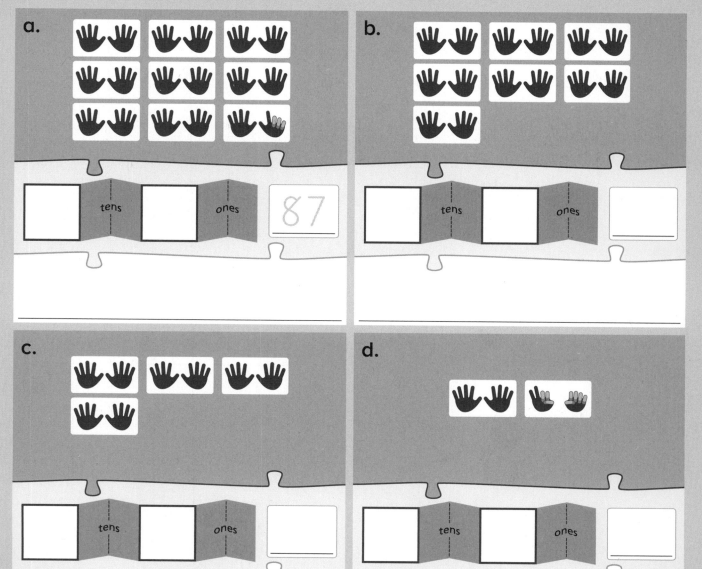

a.

| | tens | | ones | 87 |

b.

| | tens | | ones | |

c.

| | tens | | ones | |

d.

| | tens | | ones | |

Step Ahead   Count the number of tens and ones blocks.

a. Write the number.

b. Write the number name.

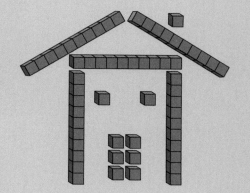

© ORIGO Education

Computation Practice   What has a face, two hands, but no legs?

★ Figure out each of these and use a ruler to draw a straight line to the matching total. The totals can be used more than once.

★ The line will pass through a number and a letter. Write each letter above its matching number at the bottom of the page.

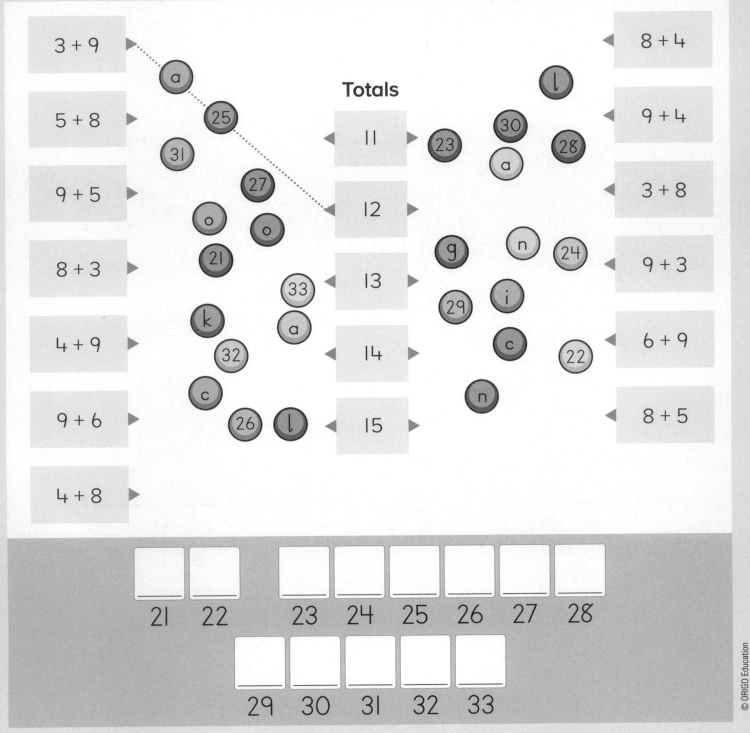

Ongoing Practice

I. **a.** Write the number that comes **just before** each of these.

| ____ | 110 | | ____ | 120 | | ____ | 130 |

b. Write the number that comes **just after** each of these.

| 105 | ____ | | 115 | ____ | | 125 | ____ |

2. Read the number name. Write the number with and without the expander.

a. seventy-two

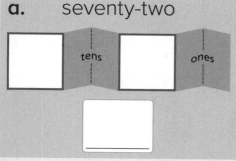

b. fifty-eight

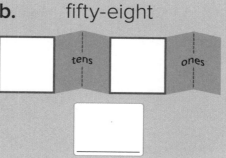

c. eighty-five

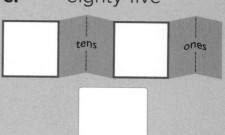

Preparing for Module 2

Write the missing numbers on these parts of a number track.

a.

9

b.
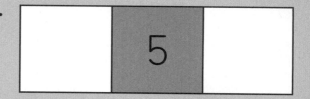
5

c.
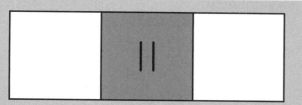
11

d.
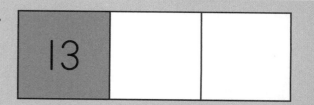
13

e.
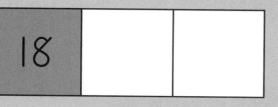
18

f.
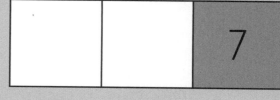
7

Step In   Look at the amounts in these purses.

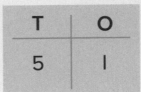

Which purse has more money?
How do you know?

Charlotte uses these place-value charts.

Which digits should she compare first?

T	O
5	1

T	O
2	6

What happens if the digits in the tens place are the same?

Write **>**, **<**, or **=** to complete this statement.

51 ◯ 26

Look at these four purses.

$44 $14 $41 $34

How would you figure out the order from **least** to **greatest**?

Step Up   1. Circle the place-value chart that shows the number that is greater. Then write **>**, **<**, or **=** to describe how the numbers compare.

a.

T	O
3	8

◯

T	O
5	2

b.

T	O
4	0

◯

T	O
1	9

c.

T	O
7	1

◯

T	O
7	6

d.

T	O
6	1

◯

T	O
1	6

2. This table shows amounts raised for charity by Grades 1 and 2. Use the table to answer this question.

Grade	Week				
	One	Two	Three	Four	Five
1	$63	$58	$39	$45	$53
2	$59	$65	$40	$57	$38

a. Write the amounts that are **less than** $50.

b. Write the amounts raised by Grade 1 in order from **greatest** to **least**.

c. Write the amounts raised by Grade 2 in order from **least** to **greatest**.

3. Write **>**, **<**, or **=** to describe how the numbers compare.

a.
82 ◯ 67

b.
42 ◯ 80

c.
18 ◯ 81

d.
39 ◯ 39

e.
92 ◯ 64

f.
15 ◯ 50

Step Ahead   Color the cards that show the numbers ordered from **greatest** to **least**.

82, 65, 90, 47	50, 47, 39, 6	69, 64, 40, 7
18, 42, 76, 80	26, 42, 38, 80	82, 82, 19, 25

Step In These number mats have been sorted into two groups.

How would you describe the sorting?

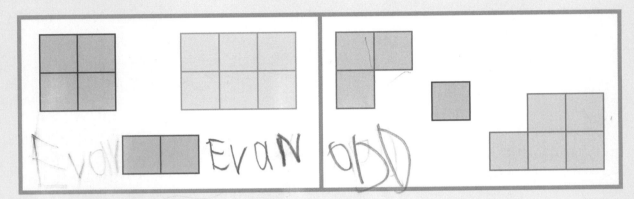

What types of numbers are in each group?

What are some other numbers you could show in each group?
How do you know?

> **Even** numbers can be shown with a *groups of two* arrangement, where every part has a partner. For **odd** numbers, there is always one left over.

Step Up

1. a. Look at the chart below. Color the even numbers red. Look at the number mats above to help.

1	2	3	4	5	6
7	8	9	10	11	12
13	14	15	16	17	18
19	20	21	22	23	24
25	26	27	28	29	30

b. Color the ○ beside each true statement.

○ You only say even numbers if you start at 0 and count by twos.

○ An even number has the digit 0, 2, 4, 6, or 8 in the ones place.

○ If you show an even number of objects in groups of two there is always one object without a partner.

2. Look at this chart.

  a. Color the odd numbers in this chart blue.

  b. Color the ⬭ beside each true statement.

  ⬭ You only say odd numbers if you start at 0 and count by fives.

  ⬭ An odd number has the digit 1, 3, 5, 7, or 9 in the ones place.

  ⬭ If you show an odd number of objects in groups of two there is always one object without a partner.

1	2	3	4	5
6	7	8	9	10
11	12	13	14	15
16	17	18	19	20
21	22	23	24	25
26	27	28	29	30

3. Write all the **even** numbers between 0 and 20.

2 6 4 8 10 200 2

4. Write all the **odd** numbers between 0 and 20.

1 5 5 9 7 3 7 2

5. Write the next two **even** numbers.

  a. 10 12 14

  b. 18 20 22

  c. 6 8 10

6. Write the next two **odd** numbers.

  a. 7 9 11

  b. 15 17 19

  c. 3 5 7

Step Ahead

Imagine that the number mats at the top of page 14 are put together. Write **odd** or **even** to complete each sentence.

  a. even number + even number = ☐ number

  b. odd number + odd number = ☐ number

  c. even number + odd number = ☐ number

Think and Solve Same shapes weigh the same.
Write the missing value inside each shape.

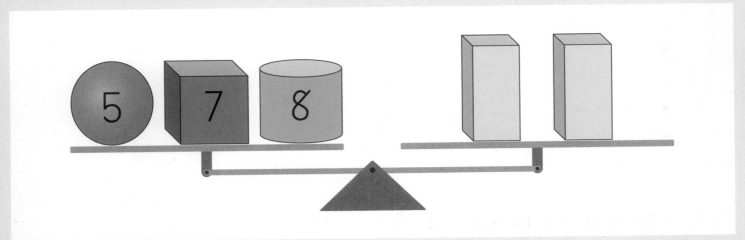

Words at Work Choose and write words from the list to complete these sentences. Each word is used only once.

even	
sixty-one	
odd	
sixteen	
sixty	
less	
greater	

a. _____ is an even number.

b. Thirteen is an _____ number.

c. Twelve is _____ than twenty-one.

d. _____ has one ten and six ones.

e. _____ is _____ than fifty-one.

f. Numbers that have 0, 2, 4, 6, or 8 in the ones place are _____ .

Ongoing Practice

I. Think about the numbers **between 1 and 50**.

a. Write all the numbers that have 5 in the ones place.

b. Write the numbers that are **2 less** than each number you wrote.

2. This table shows money raised for charity.

Week	One	Two	Three	Four	Five
Amount	$39	$45	$41	$36	$27

a. Write the amounts that are **less than** $40.

b. Write the amounts in order from **greatest** to **least**.

_____ , _____ , _____ , _____ , _____

Preparing for Module 2

Write the matching number of tens and ones on the expander. Then write the matching number name.

a.
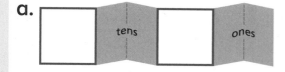

b.
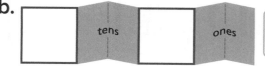

Step In

Where have you seen or heard one hundred?

My great-grandmother is 100 years old.

There are 100 cents in one dollar.

What are some different ways you could show **one hundred**?

How could you show one hundred using blocks like these?
How many tens blocks would you need?
How many ones blocks would you need?
What other block could you use?

What different ways could you show **125** using blocks?

I hundreds block, 2 tens, and 5 ones, or

12 tens and 5 ones, or

125 ones.

Step Up

I. Circle groups of 10 tens blocks to make one hundred. Write the number of hundreds. Then write the number of tens and ones left over.

a.

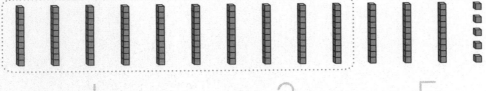

___1___ hundred ___3___ tens ___5___ ones

b.

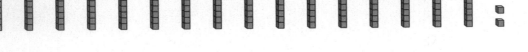

_____ hundred _____ tens _____ ones

2. Circle groups of 10 tens blocks to make one hundred.
Then write the number of hundreds, tens, and ones.

a.

_____ hundreds   _____ tens   _____ ones

b.

_____ hundreds   _____ tens   _____ ones

c.

_____ hundreds   _____ tens   _____ ones

d.

_____ hundreds   _____ tens   _____ ones

Step Ahead   Write the missing numbers.

a. | 1 hundred 4 tens 7 ones | **is equal to** | _____ tens _____ ones |

b. | 3 hundreds 4 tens 5 ones | **is equal to** | _____ tens _____ ones |

c. | 3 hundreds 4 tens 0 ones | **is equal to** | _____ tens _____ ones |

Step In

What number is shown by this picture of blocks?

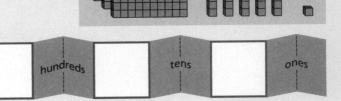

How do you know?

How could you write the same number on this expander?

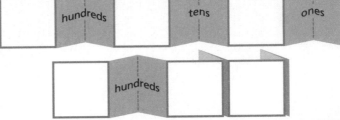

How do you read the number?
What parts of the number do you say together?

How would you read and say these numbers?

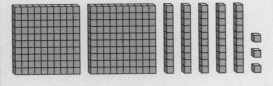

Step Up

I. Look at these pictures of blocks. Write the matching number on the expanders.

a.

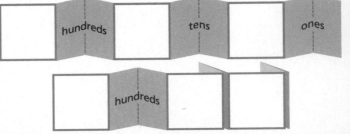

b.

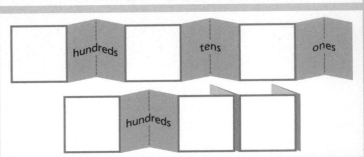

c.

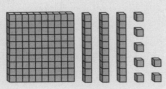

2. Color blocks to show the number on the expander.

a.

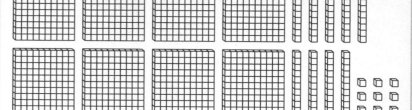

b.

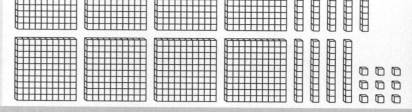

c.

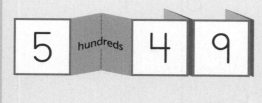

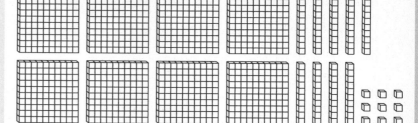

d.

Step Ahead Color more blocks to match the number on the expander.

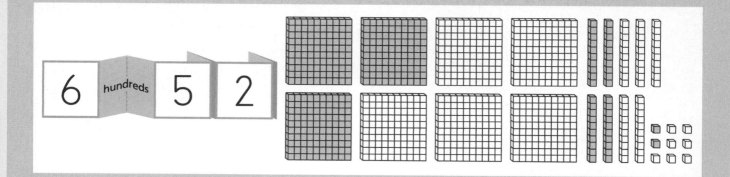

Computation Practice   **What can you not eat for breakfast?**

★ Write all the totals.

★ Write the letter in each box above its matching total at the bottom of the page.

7 + 5 = 12   n   8 + 9 = ☐   h

3 + 4 = ☐   i   5 + 3 = ☐   n

2 + 3 = ☐   r   6 + 5 = ☐   e

8 + 7 = ☐   l   2 + 4 = ☐   u

6 + 8 = ☐   d   7 + 6 = ☐   d

6 + 4 = ☐   a   3 + 1 = ☐   c

7 + 9 = ☐   n   5 + 4 = ☐   n

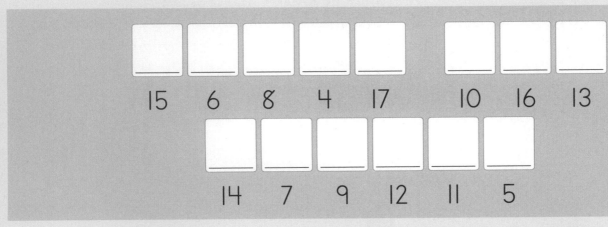

☐ ☐ ☐ ☐ ☐   ☐ ☐ ☐
15 6 8 4 17   10 16 13

☐ ☐ ☐ ☐ ☐ ☐
14 7 9 12 11 5

Ongoing Practice

1. Write the answers. Draw jumps on the number track to help you.

| 65 | 66 | 67 | 68 | 69 | 70 | 71 | 72 | 73 | 74 | 75 |

a. 73 – 1 = ☐

b. 68 – 2 = ☐

c. 71 – 3 = ☐

2. Circle a group of tens blocks to make one hundred. Write the number of hundreds. Then write the number of tens and ones left over.

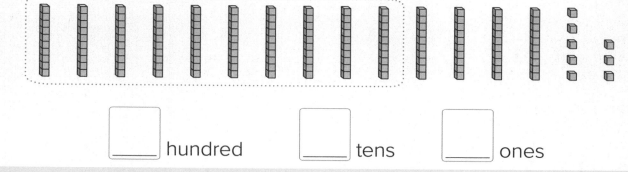

☐ hundred   ☐ tens   ☐ ones

Preparing for Module 2

Compare the numbers in the charts. Circle the words that are true.

a.

Tens	Ones
7	5

is greater than

is less than

Tens	Ones
5	2

b.

Tens	Ones
4	6

is greater than

is less than

Tens	Ones
5	0

Step In

What number is shown on this expander?

| 1 | hundreds | 6 | 3 |

How do you read the number?

What parts of the expander do you read together?

Which of these words would you use to write the matching number name?

ten	twenty	thirty
forty	fifty	sixty
seventy	eighty	ninety

one	two	three
four	five	six
seven	eight	nine

_____ hundred _____

Step Up

1. Look at the blocks. Write the matching number on the expander.

a.
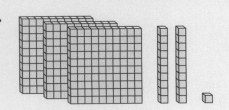   hundreds

b.
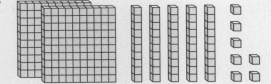   hundreds

c.
   hundreds

2. Look at the blocks. Write the number on the expander.
Then complete the number name.

a.

_____ hundred _____

b.

_____ hundred _____

c.

_____ hundred _____

Step Ahead

Look at these two pictures of blocks. Figure out the **total** of the two numbers they show. Then write the total in words.

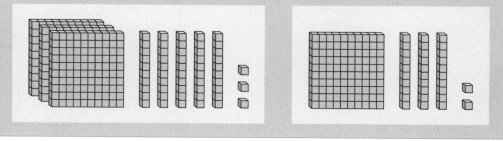

_____

Step In

How could you figure out the number shown in this picture of blocks?

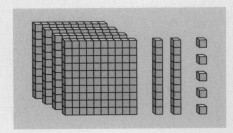

I add the places in my head like this. 400 + 20 + 5 = 425

hundreds

How would you write the same number on these expanders?

How would you write the number without an expander?

Look at the picture of blocks above.

How many of each type of block must be added to create **this number**? How do you know?

7 4 6

Step Up

1. Look at the picture of blocks. Write the matching number on the expanders.

a.

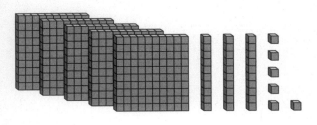

hundreds

b.

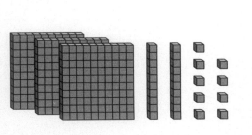

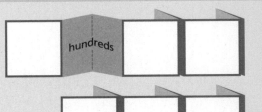

hundreds

2. Write the matching number with and without the expander.

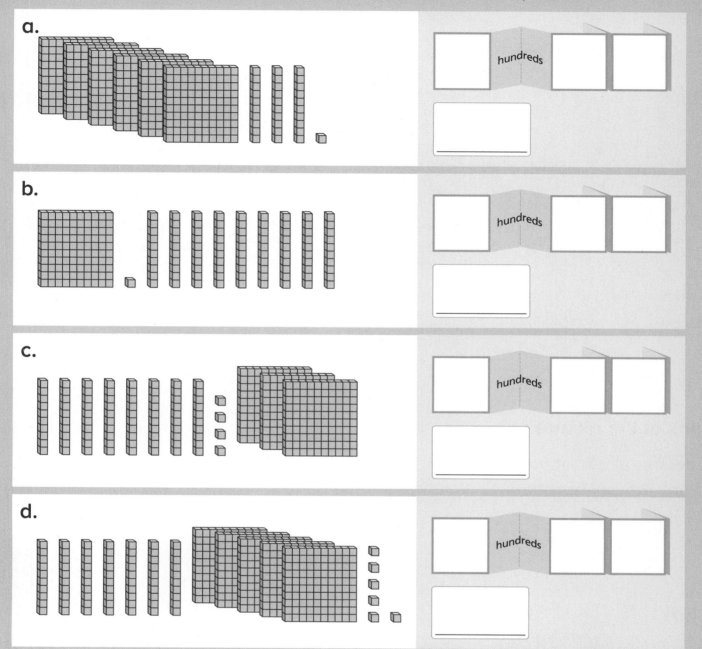

a.

hundreds

b.

hundreds

c.

hundreds

d.

hundreds

Step Ahead   Write the number to match the picture of blocks.

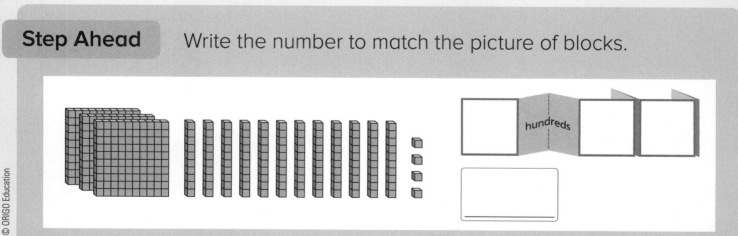

hundreds

Think and Solve Imagine that the pattern continues.

Picture   1   2   3   4

a. How many dots will be in Picture 10? _____

b. Which picture will have 25 dots? _____

Words at Work   Write a number that is greater than 30 but less than 35. _____

Write some things that you know about your number.
Use words from the list to help you.

| even |
| double |
| greater than |
| half |
| less than |
| odd |
| ones |
| tens |
| thirty |

_____

_____

_____

_____

_____

_____

1. Write the differences. You can use this piece of hundred chart to help.

a. 54 – 20 = _____

b. 37 – 10 = _____

c. 42 – 30 = _____

d. 58 – 40 = _____

e. 33 – 20 = _____

1	2	3	4	5	6	7	8	9	10
11	12	13	14	15	16	17	18	19	20
21	22	23	24	25	26	27	28	29	30
31	32	33	34	35	36	37	38	39	40
41	42	43	44	45	46	47	48	49	50
51	52	53	54	55	56	57	58	59	60

2. Look at the picture of blocks. Write the matching number on the expander. Then complete the number name.

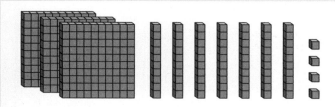

hundreds

_____ hundred _____

Write the time shown on each clock.

a.

_____ o'clock

b.

_____ o'clock

c.

_____ o'clock

Step In What addition story could you say about this picture?

Which number is the **total** in your story? How do you know?

Which numbers are **parts** of the total? How do you know?

What addition fact could you write to match your story? $3 + 2 = 5$

Step Up 1. Write numbers to match each picture.
Then write the addition fact.

a.

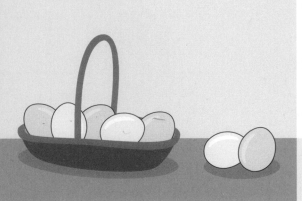

There are __5__ eggs in the basket.

There are __2__ eggs out of the basket.

There are __7__ eggs in total.

$5 + 2 = 7$ ✓

b.

__4__ coins are in the jar. ✓

__1__ more coin is dropped in the jar.

There are __4__ coins in total.

$1 + 4 = 5$

2. Add the groups. Then write an addition fact to match.

a.

_____

b.

_____

c.

_____

d.

_____

3. Read the story. Then write an addition fact to match.

a. Cathy has 6 raspberries and 2 strawberries. How many berries does she have in total?

8 + c

b. Hugo has eaten 7 olives and has 2 more to eat. How many olives did he have in total?

Step Ahead

Write numbers to complete different number facts. Make each total **less than** 10.

$7 + 3 = 10$ $7 = 3 + 10$ $7 + 3 = 10$

$7 = 3 + 10$ $7 + 3 = 10$ $7 = 3 + 10$

Step In What numbers have been rolled on these number cubes?

How would you figure out the total of the two numbers?

Write an addition fact to match.

It's easier to start with six and count on two more. That's **6**.... 7, 8. 6 + 2 = 8.

What are some other totals that you could roll?

Step Up I. Write the addition fact to match each card.

a.

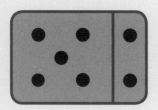

b.

c.

d.

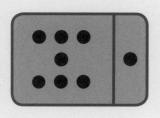

e.

f.

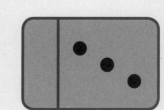

2. Write the addition fact to match each of these.

a.

____ + ____ = ____

b.

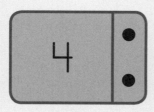

____ + ____ = ____

c.

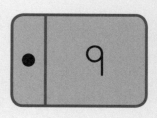

____ + ____ = ____

d.

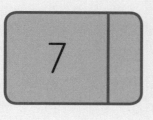

____ + ____ = ____

e.

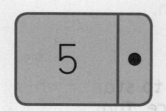

____ + ____ = ____

f.

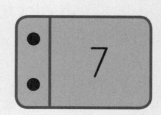

____ + ____ = ____

3. Count on 1 or 2 to figure out the total. Then write the addition equation.

a.

____ + ____ = ____

b.

____ + ____ = ____

c.

____ + ____ = ____

Step Ahead   Complete each equation. Use the number track to help.

a. $14 + 2 =$ ⬜

| 10 | 11 | 12 | 13 | **14** | 15 | 16 | 17 | 18 | 19 |

b. $16 + 3 =$ ⬜

| 10 | 11 | 12 | 13 | 14 | 15 | **16** | 17 | 18 | 19 |

Computation Practice

★ Draw a ✔ beside each correct answer on Jennifer's test paper.
★ Count each ✔ and write the total at the bottom of the page.

Correct the facts that were wrong.

Name: Jennifer

a. $5 + 4 =$ 9

b. $7 + 8 =$ 15

c. $7 + 6 =$ 14

d. $8 + 9 =$ 16

e. $2 + 3 =$ 5

f. $6 + 5 =$ 11

g. $3 + 4 =$ 17

h. $3 + 2 =$ 5

i. $9 + 8 =$ 16

j. $4 + 3 =$ 7

k. $4 + 5 =$ 8

l. $8 + 7 =$ 15

m. $5 + 6 =$ 11

n. $6 + 7 =$ 14

Total correct: _____

© ORIGO Education

I. Circle the container with the **smaller** capacity.

a.

b.

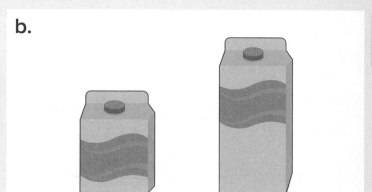

FROM 1.12.9

2. Add the groups. Then write an addition fact to match.

a.

_____

b.

_____

FROM 2.1.9

Preparing for Module 2   Write the time shown on each clock.

a.

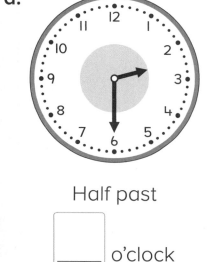

Half past

☐ o'clock

b.

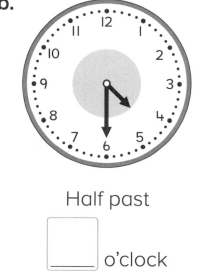

Half past

☐ o'clock

c.

Half past

☐ o'clock

Step In   Carmen has seven games.

Her mom buys her two more games.

How many games does she now have?

What addition fact would you write?

_____

Mateo has eight games. He buys some more games.
He now has 11 games. How many games did he buy?

> I could use addition or subtraction to solve
> this problem. That's 8 + ___ = 11, or 11 – 8 = ___.

Step Up   1.   Write an equation to match each problem.
Use a **?** to show the unknown amount.

a. Cary buys 2 games. The first game costs $2. The second game costs $4. What is the total cost of the games?	b. Jacinta buys 3 games for a total of $10. The first game was $9. The second game was free. What was the cost of the third game?
_____ = _____	_____ = _____
c. Emily has 6 games. Ethan has 2 more games than Emily. How many games does Ethan have?	d. Michelle completes the final level of a game and earns 3 more stars. She now has 10 stars. How many stars did she have before?
_____ = _____	_____ = _____

2. Solve each problem. Show your thinking.

a. Sara finished a level of a game in 8 minutes. Eva took one minute more to finish the same level. How long did it take Eva?

_____ minutes

b. 5 students wait to play a game. 3 of the students are girls. How many boys are waiting?

_____ boys

c. Kayla played a game for 15 minutes. Harvey played for 2 minutes more. How long did Harvey play the game for?

_____ minutes

d. Juan is given 2 racing games. He now has 13 racing games in total. How many racing games did he have before?

_____ games

Step Ahead
Count on 1, 2, or 3 to figure out the total. Then write the total.

a. $11 + 2 =$ ☐

b. $3 + 16 =$ ☐

c. $18 + 2 =$ ☐

d. $23 + 1 =$ ☐

e. $2 + 27 =$ ☐

f. $25 + 3 =$ ☐

g. $3 + 32 =$ ☐

h. $34 + 3 =$ ☐

i. $1 + 33 =$ ☐

Step In   Look at these pictures. What do you notice?

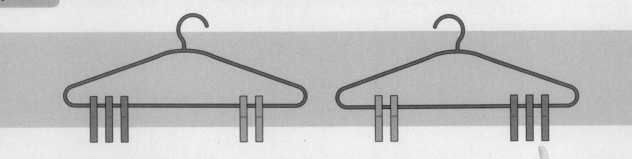

What addition facts could you write to match the pictures?

What do you call a pair of facts like this?

These are called turnaround facts. Turnaround facts have the same parts and the same total.

Step Up   1.   Write two addition facts to match each picture.

a.

$4 + 2 = \boxed{}$

$2 + 4 = \boxed{}$

b.
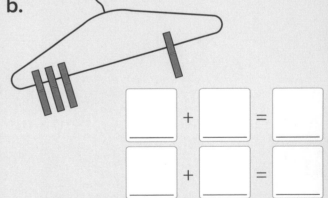

$\boxed{} + \boxed{} = \boxed{}$

$\boxed{} + \boxed{} = \boxed{}$

c.
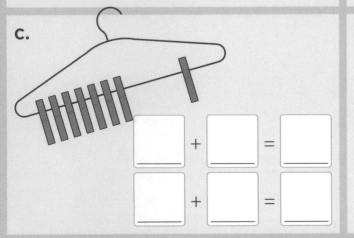

$\boxed{} + \boxed{} = \boxed{}$

$\boxed{} + \boxed{} = \boxed{}$

d.
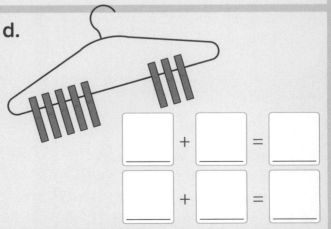

$\boxed{} + \boxed{} = \boxed{}$

$\boxed{} + \boxed{} = \boxed{}$

2. Draw lines to join matching turnaround facts.
Cross out the facts that do not have a match.

$8 + 3 = 11$	$7 + 2 = 9$
$1 + 6 = 7$	$4 + 1 = 5$
$2 + 7 = 9$	$3 + 8 = 11$
$0 + 8 = 8$	$1 + 8 = 9$
$8 + 1 = 9$	$8 + 0 = 8$

3. Write **true** or **false**.

a. $5 + 0 = 5$
is the turnaround for
$0 + 5 = 5$

b. $3 + 9 = 12$
is the turnaround for
$12 + 9 = 3$

c. $6 + 2 = 8$
is the turnaround for
$4 + 4 = 8$

d. $4 + 1 = 5$
is the turnaround for
$1 + 4 = 5$

e. $2 + 8 = 10$
is the turnaround for
$4 + 6 = 10$

f. $0 + 3 = 3$
is the turnaround for
$3 + 3 = 0$

Step Ahead   Write the turnaround sentences to match.

a. $14 + 2 = 16$

☐ + ☐ = ☐

b. $3 + 12 = 15$

☐ + ☐ = ☐

c. $17 + 0 = 17$

☐ + ☐ = ☐

Think and Solve

Imagine you threw three beanbags and they all landed on this target. Add the numbers in your head.

a. What is the greatest total you can get? ☐

b. What is the least total you can get? ☐

c. Write an equation to show one way you can make a **total of 12**.

d. Write equations to show **two other ways** you can make a total of 12.

Words at Work

Write a word problem that you would solve by using the count-on addition strategy. You can use words from the list to help.

| add |
| figure out |
| how many |
| total |
| one more |
| two more |

ORIGO Stepping Stones • Grade 2 • 1.12

© ORIGO Education

Ongoing Practice

1. Write the number of scoops of water for each container. Then circle the container that holds the most.

Container	Number of Scoops of Water	
a.		_____ scoops
b.		_____ scoops

2. Solve each problem. Show your thinking.

a. Nam has 12 marbles in total. 9 of the marbles are blue and the rest are green. How many green marbles does Nam have?

_____ green marbles

b. Kylie has 8 trading cards. Corey has 3 more cards than Kylie. How many cards does Corey have?

_____ cards

Preparing for Module 2   Write the answers.

a. Double 8 is [ ]

b. Double 7 is [ ]

c. Double 6 is [ ]

d. Double 9 is [ ]

e. Double 4 is [ ]

f. Double 5 is [ ]

Step In

Look at this part of a number track.

| | | | | | 30 | | | | | | | | | | | 40 | | | | |

What number would you write in the position shown by the arrow?
How do you know?

How can you figure out where each of these is located on the number track?

42   37   29

Step Up

1. Draw a line to show where each number and number name is located on the track.

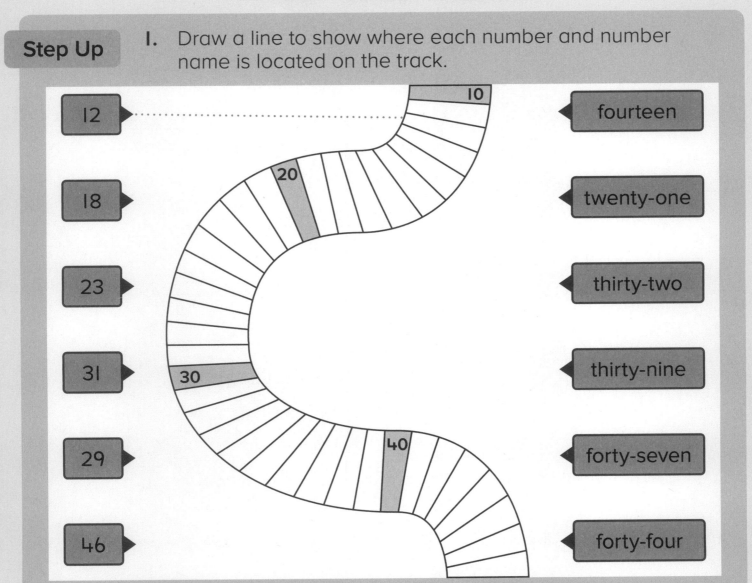

12   fourteen

18   twenty-one

23   thirty-two

31   thirty-nine

29   forty-seven

46   forty-four

2. Write the number that should be shown in these positions.

a.

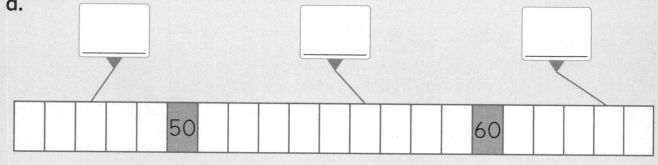

b.

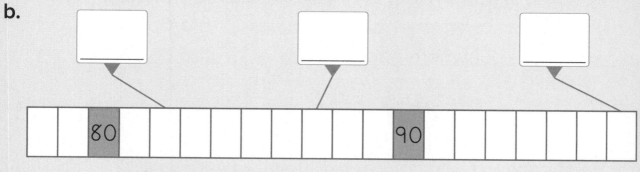

c.

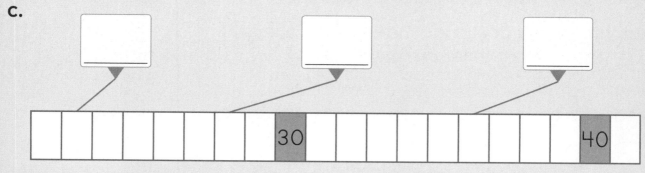

Look at this part of a number track.

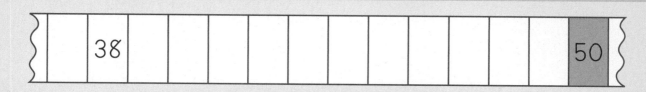

Circle the numbers that you could show on this part of a number track.

| 40 | 44 | 42 | 35 | 49 | 52 |

Step In Look at the number track.

What number would you write in the position that is shaded?
How do you know?

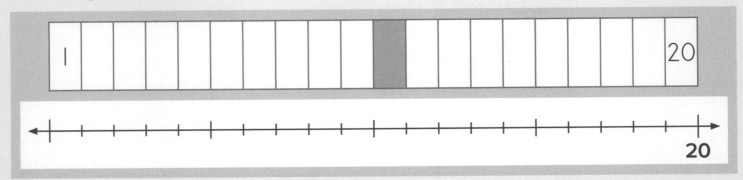

Look at the number line above.
How is it the same as the number track? How is it different?
Where should we write **0** on the number line?

What do you notice about the marks along the number line?
What do the marks of different length show? How do you know?

Which mark on the number line shows the same number
that is shaded on the number track? How do you know?

What is a quick way to find 17 on the number line?

Step Up   1. Draw jumps to show the position of each number
on the number line.

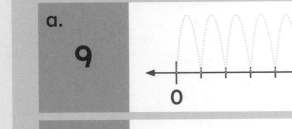

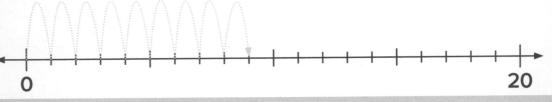

a.

9

b.

14

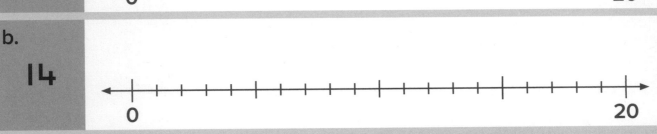

2. Draw a line from each number to its position on the number line.

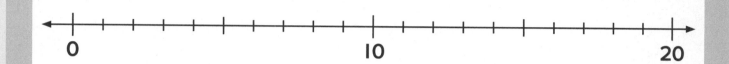

a. 5   b. 3   c. 9   d. 18

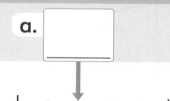 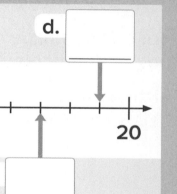

e. 1   f. 11   g. 7   h. 15

3. Write the number that should be shown in each position.

a. [　]   b. [　]   c. [　]   d. [　]

0   10   20

e. [　]   f. [　]   g. [　]   h. [　]

Step Ahead

Imagine that you showed each of these numbers on a number line. Color the number in each pair that would be the **greater** distance from zero.

a. 7 — 11   b. 9 — 3   c. 10 — 16

d. 16 — 15   e. 8 — 12   f. 17 — 20

Computation Practice   What is hiding in the puzzle below?

★ Write all the totals.
★ Find each total in the puzzle and color those parts black.
★ Color all the other numbered parts green.

5 + 5 = ☐   1 + 2 = ☐   8 + 1 = ☐

7 + 8 = ☐   3 + 4 = ☐   9 + 9 = ☐

2 + 2 = ☐   1 + 5 = ☐   9 + 10 = ☐

4 + 1 = ☐   5 + 7 = ☐   8 + 8 = ☐

One part has no number. Leave this white.

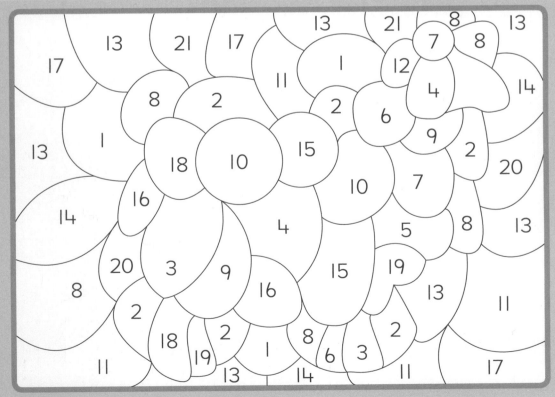

Ongoing Practice

1. Write the number of tens and ones on the expander. Then write the matching number name.

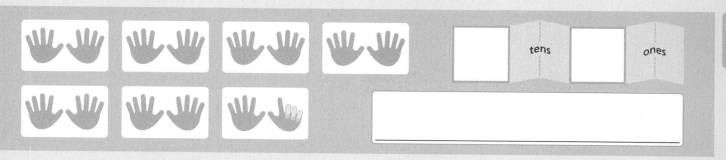

2. Write the numbers in these positions.

a.

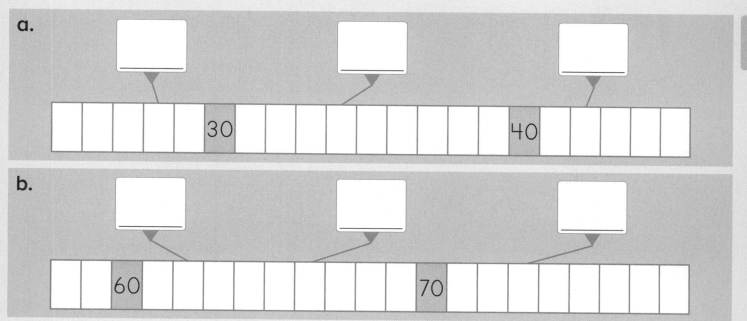

b.

Preparing for Module 3

Color the blocks to match the number shown on each expander.

a.

| 1 | hundreds | 0 | 9 |

b.

| 1 | hundreds | 0 | 3 |

Step In What can you tell about this number line?

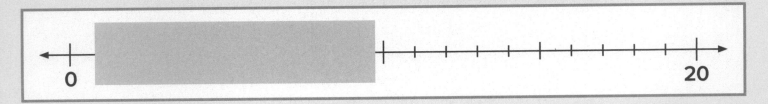

What numbers are covered?

Number lines can begin at a number other than zero. The number line below starts at 50.

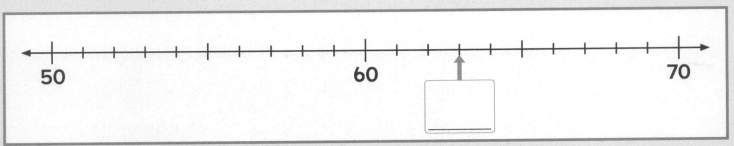

What number would you write in the empty box? How did you decide?

What other numbers could you show on this number line?

Step Up

1. Draw a line from each number to its position on the number line.

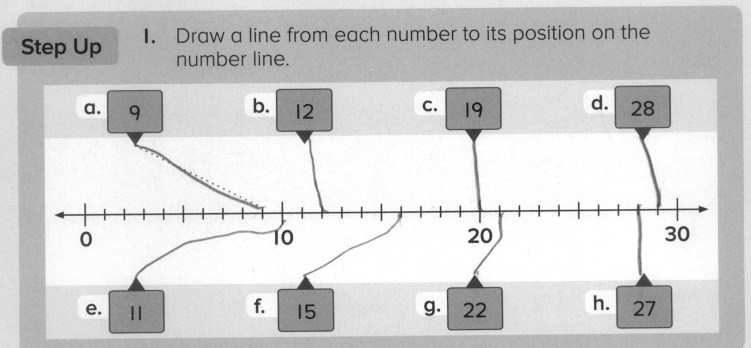

a. 9   b. 12   c. 19   d. 28

e. 11   f. 15   g. 22   h. 27

2. Draw a line from each number to its position on the number line.

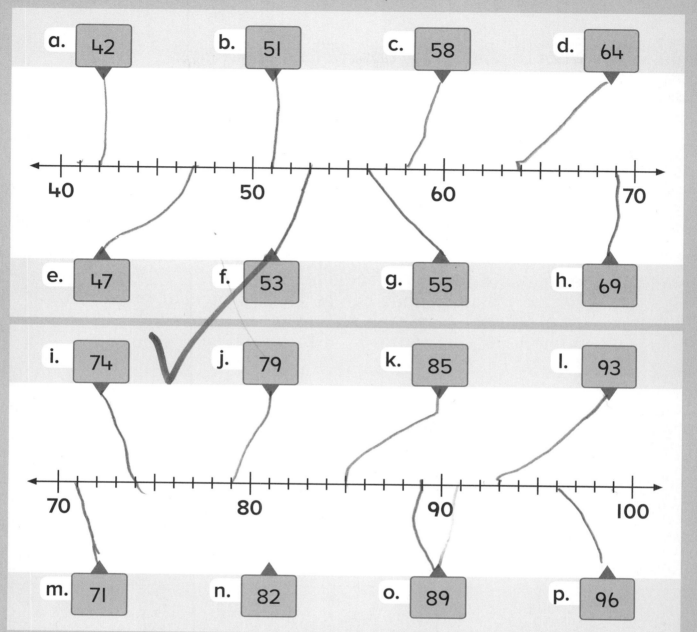

a. 42 b. 51 c. 58 d. 64

40   50   60   70

e. 47 f. 53 g. 55 h. 69

i. 74 j. 79 k. 85 l. 93

70   80   90   100

m. 71 n. 82 o. 89 p. 96

Step Ahead

Draw a line from each number to its position on the number line. Think carefully before you draw.

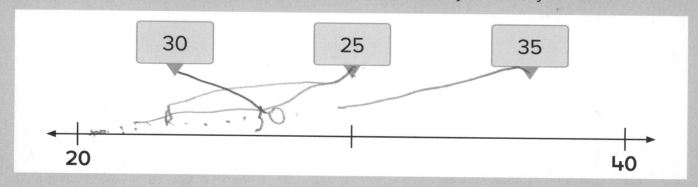

30   25   35

20   40

Step In   **What do you notice about this number line?**

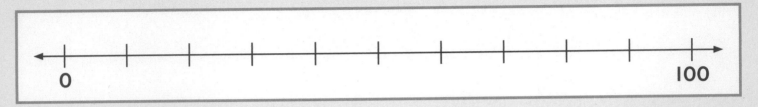

0   100

This number line has been broken into 10 equal parts. What number would you write below each mark?

Where is 47 on the number line?
Which ten is closer?
How far away is 47 from the closest ten?

Imagine you placed a ball on this special number line.

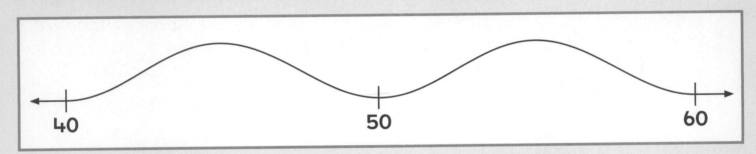

40   50   60

How could the ball help you decide which ten is closest to 54?

Step Up   **I.   For each number, write the ten that is closest.**

30   32   · 36   40   50

a.
32
_30_

b.
36
_40_

c.
43
_44_

d.
47
_48_

e.
49
_50_

2. Write the **ten** that is closest. You can draw lines to help.

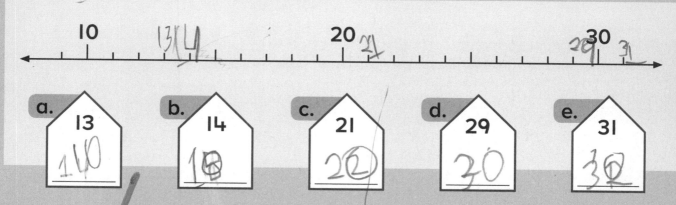

a. 13   b. 14   c. 21   d. 29   e. 31

3. Write **how far away** each number is from the nearest ten.
You can draw lines to help you.

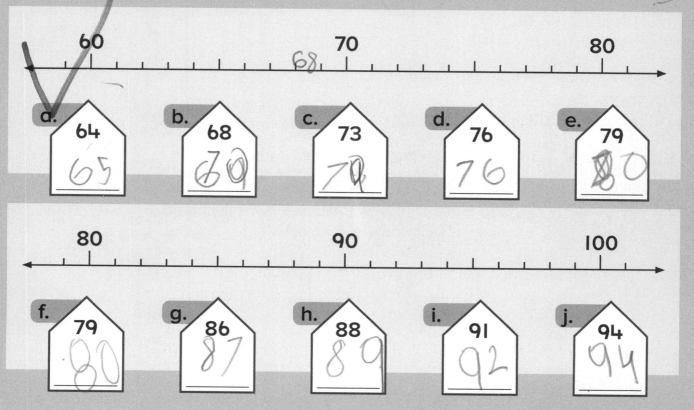

a. 64   b. 68   c. 73   d. 76   e. 79

f. 79   g. 86   h. 88   i. 91   j. 94

Step Ahead

Write two two-digit numbers that do **not** have a 0 or a 5.
Then complete the sentences. Use the number lines above
to help.

a. ☐☐   The distance to the nearest ten is ☐.

b. ☐☐   The distance to the nearest ten is ☐.

Think and Solve Write how you can use **the 2 buckets** to get exactly 5 scoops of water into the tub.

Buckets

1 scoop   6 scoops

Tub

Words at Work   Write in words how you solve this problem. You can use words from the list to help you.

There are 3 horses and some chickens on a farm.
There is a total of 18 legs. How many animals are there in total?

add

figure out

steps of

total

count

Ongoing Practice

1. **a.** Write the next two **even** numbers.

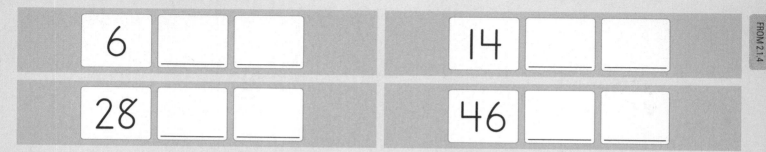

| 6 | ___ | ___ |

| 14 | ___ | ___ |

| 28 | ___ | ___ |

| 46 | ___ | ___ |

b. Write the next two **odd** numbers.

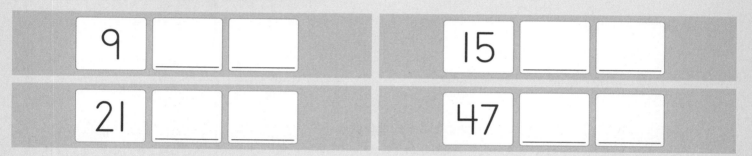

| 9 | ___ | ___ |

| 15 | ___ | ___ |

| 21 | ___ | ___ |

| 47 | ___ | ___ |

2. Draw a line from each number to its position on the number line.

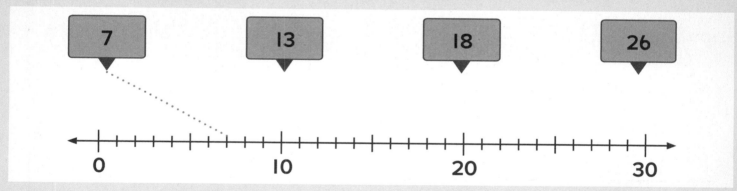

| 7 | 13 | 18 | 26 |

0   10   20   30

Preparing for Module 3

Look at the picture of blocks. Write the number on the expanders. Then write the matching number name.

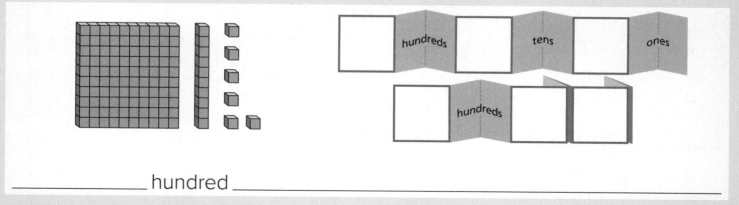

hundreds   tens   ones

hundreds

_____ hundred _____

Step In Look at this number line.

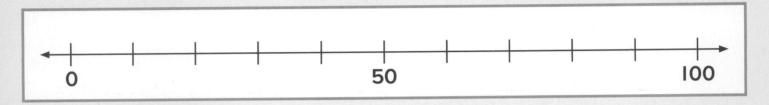

Trace your finger along the part of the number line that shows numbers that are equal to or greater than 50.

Trace your finger along the part of the number line that shows numbers that are equal to or less than 30.

Show the position of these two numbers. 45 62

Which number is greater? How did you decide?

> The distance from 0 to 62 is greater than the distance from 0 to 45.

Step Up I. Color the part of the number line that shows each of these.

a. Numbers equal to or greater than 70

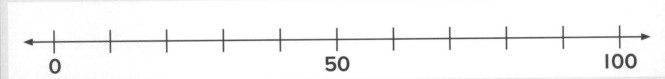

b. Numbers equal to or less than 80

2. Write **<** or **>** in each circle to describe each pair of numbers. Draw a line to join each number to its position on the number line to help your thinking.

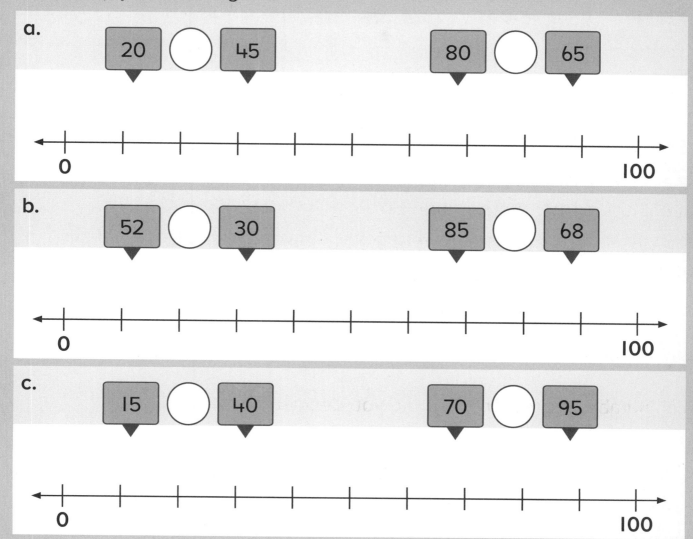

a.
20 ◯ 45   80 ◯ 65

b.
52 ◯ 30   85 ◯ 68

c.
15 ◯ 40   70 ◯ 95

Step Ahead

Helen colors the number line to match the instructions on one of the cards. Circle the card that she chose.

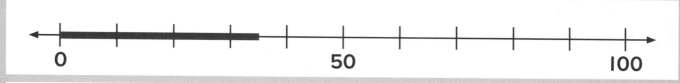

| Color red all numbers that are between 10 and 50. | Color red all numbers that are equal to or greater than 50. | Color red all numbers that are equal to or less than 35. |

Step In This is an empty number line. There are no numbers labeled.

How could you show the position of these two numbers on the empty number line?

| 74 | 56 |

Hannah labels the empty number line to start at 0 and end at 100.

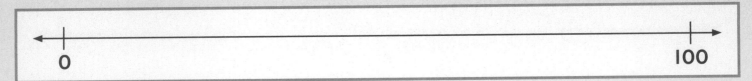

How does this help her identify the position of the two numbers? What other numbers could she label?

Blake uses a different method. He labels the empty number line to start at 50 and end at 80.

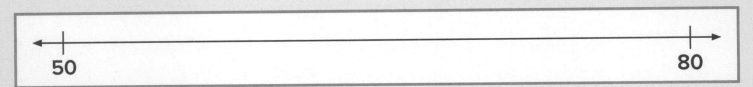

Why did he choose these two numbers? What other numbers could he label? Which method do you prefer?

Step Up

1. Show the position of each number. You can break the number line into more parts to help your thinking.

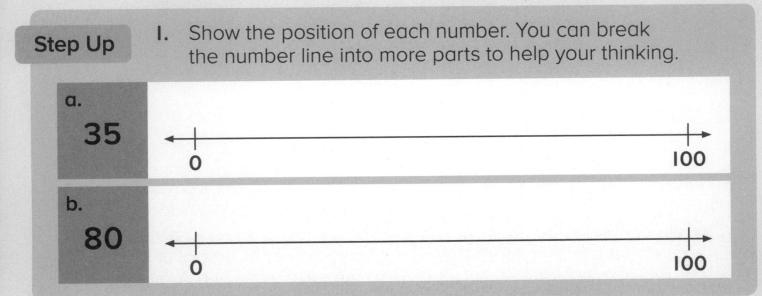

a. 35

b. 80

2. Use Hannah's strategy to show the position of each number.

a.

70

0

b.

25

0

c.

59

0

d.

10

0

e.

46

0

f.

63

0

Step Ahead Use Blake's strategy to show the position of each pair of numbers.

a.

32   45

b.

96   85

Computation Practice

I have one head, one foot, and four legs. What am I?

★ Write all the answers, then color the parts in the puzzle that match.

$14 - 6 =$ ☐ $7 + 8 =$ ☐ $9 + 3 =$ ☐

$11 - 5 =$ ☐ $2 - 2 =$ ☐ $4 + 9 =$ ☐

$8 + 6 =$ ☐ $6 - 1 =$ ☐ $7 - 3 =$ ☐

$7 + 9 =$ ☐ $6 + 5 =$ ☐ $17 - 8 =$ ☐

$8 - 5 =$ ☐ $3 + 7 =$ ☐ $9 + 8 =$ ☐

$4 - 3 =$ ☐

ORIGO Stepping Stones • Grade 2 • 2.6

Ongoing Practice

1. Write the addition fact to match each card.

a.
8 • •

___ + ___ = ___

b.
• 6

___ + ___ = ___

c.
5 • •

___ + ___ = ___

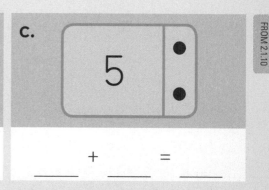

2. Draw a line to join each number to its position on the number line.
Then write **<** or **>** in each circle to describe each pair of numbers.

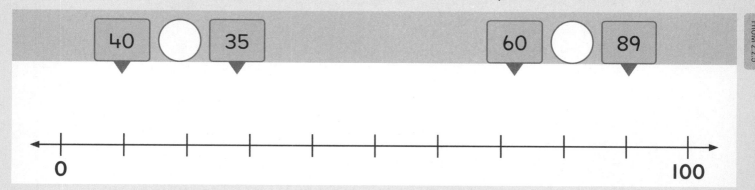

40 ◯ 35   60 ◯ 89

0   100

Preparing for Module 3

Look at the picture of blocks. Write the matching
number with and without the place-value chart.

a.
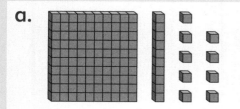

Hundreds	Tens	Ones

___

b.

Hundreds	Tens	Ones

___

c.

Hundreds	Tens	Ones

___

Step In What time does this clock show?

How do you know?

How would you write the time in words?

How would you show the same time on this digital clock?

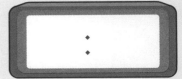

Step Up I. Write each time on the digital clock.

a.

b.

c.

d.

e.

f.

2. Draw the clock hands to show these times.

a.
9 o'clock

b.
1 o'clock

c.
5 o'clock

3. Write these times on the digital clocks.

a.
6 o'clock

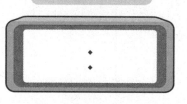

b.
12 o'clock

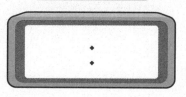

c.
3 o'clock

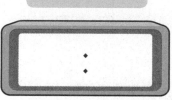

d.
11 o'clock

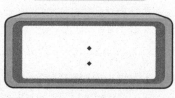

Step Ahead

Look at the analog clock. Write the time that is **one hour before** and the time that is **one hour after**.

one hour before

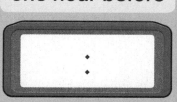

one hour after

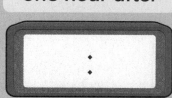

Step In **Look at this analog clock.**

What does the long hand tell you?
What does the short hand tell you?
What time is shown on the clock?

Look at this digital clock.
What do the numbers on the left side of the colon tell you?
What do the numbers on the right side of the colon tell you?
What time is shown on the clock?

How many minutes are in one hour?
How many minutes are in half an hour? How do you know?

Look at these two clocks.

What times are they showing?
How do you know?

Step Up

I. Circle in **red** all the clocks that show a time **on the hour**.
Circle in **blue** all the clocks that show a time **half-past the hour**.

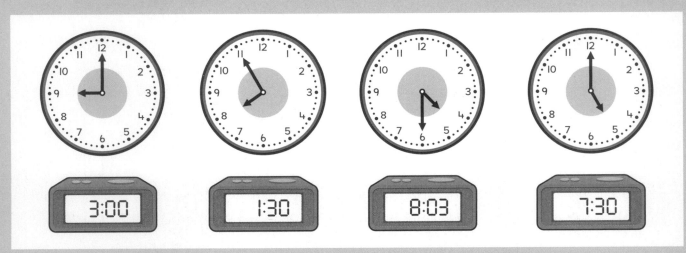

© ORIGO Education

2. Write each time in words.

a.

_____

_____

b.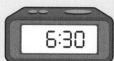

_____

_____

c.

_____

_____

d.

12:30

_____

_____

e.

6:30

_____

_____

f.

4:00

_____

_____

g.

_____

_____

h.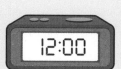

12:00

_____

_____

i.

_____

_____

Step Ahead

Circle the clocks that show a time after 11 o'clock in the morning and before half-past 4 in the afternoon.

5:30

11:30

12:00

1:00

Think and Solve Look at these three strings.

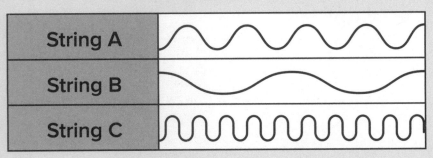

String A	
String B	
String C	

Complete these sentences.

a. String [ ] is the **longest**.

b. String [ ] is the **shortest**.

Words at Work — Write the answer for each clue in the grid. Use words from the list.

Clues Across

2. An empty number line does not have any ___ on it.

4. A number ___ does not have to start at zero.

5. Eighteen is ___ to twenty than ten.

Clues Down

1. There are thirty minutes in ___ an hour.

2. The long hand on a clock counts the ___.

3. There are ___ minutes in one hour.

closer

line

marks

sixty

half

minutes

Ongoing Practice

1. Write two addition facts to match each picture.

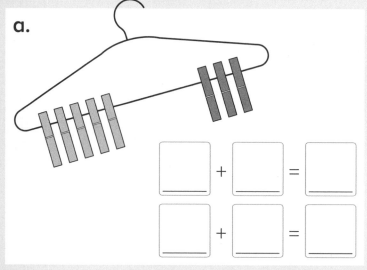

a.

☐ + ☐ = ☐

☐ + ☐ = ☐

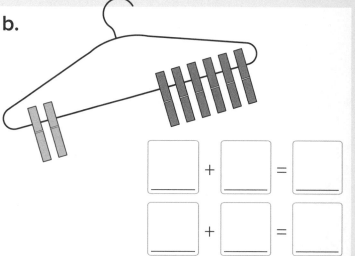

b.

☐ + ☐ = ☐

☐ + ☐ = ☐

2. Draw the clock hands to show these times.

a.

3 o'clock

b.

11 o'clock

c.

7 o'clock

Preparing for Module 3

Compare the numerals. Write **is greater than** or **is less than** to make true statements.

a.

46 ☐ 50

b.

33 ☐ 13

Step In

Kevin is playing a matching game.
Which cards should he match?

Do you know another way to say half-past 2?

Some people say
"two-thirty."

Step Up

1. Draw lines to connect the matching times.
   Cross out the digital clock that does not have a match.

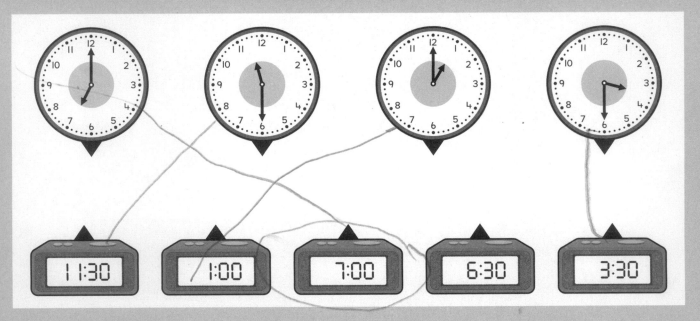

2. Draw lines to connect clocks to times.
Cross out the two clocks that do **not** have a match.

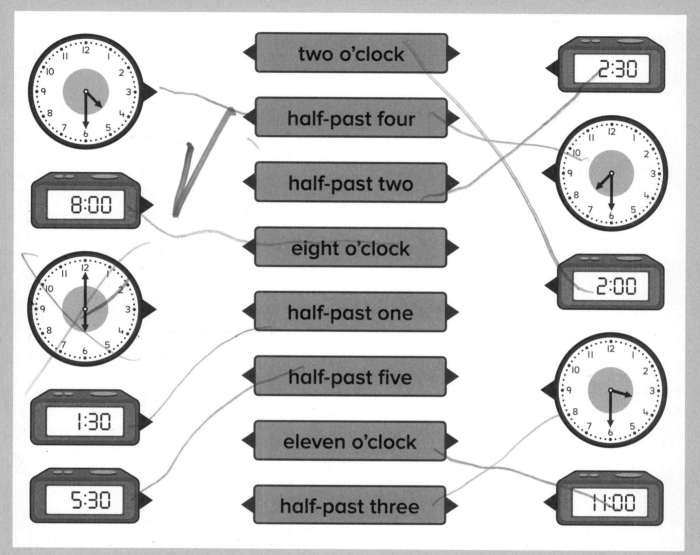

| two o'clock |
| half-past four |
| half-past two |
| eight o'clock |
| half-past one |
| half-past five |
| eleven o'clock |
| half-past three |

Step Ahead Some information is missing from these clocks.
Figure out each time.

a.

10:00

b.

4:00

© ORIGO Education

Step In Some friends are playing a game where they double the number that they roll on a number cube.

How would you figure out double 7?

Manuel does not know double 7, but he does know double 5.
He figures out the answer like this.

> Double 5 is 10
> Double 2 is 4
> **SO**
> Double 7 is 14

How did Manuel figure out the answer?

What is another double you could figure out in the same way?

Step Up 1. Use the same strategy to figure out each of these.

a. **Double 8**

Double 5 is ☐
Double 3 is ☐
SO
Double 8 is ☐

b. **Double 9**

Double 5 is ☐
Double 4 is ☐
SO
Double 9 is ☐

c. **Double 6**

Double 5 is ☐
Double 1 is ☐
SO
Double 6 is ☐

2. Play this doubling game with another student.

   a. Take turns to roll a cube labeled 4, 5, 6, 7, 8, and 9.

   b. Double the number that you roll. Then place a counter on the total in the strip below.

   c. The first student to cover all the totals wins.

8	10	12	14	16	18

3. Color the ⬭ beside the statement that you think is true. Try to draw a picture to prove your answer.

   ⬭ If you double a number from 1 to 9, the total is always odd.

   ⬭ If you double a number from 1 to 9, the total is always even.

   ⬭ If you double a number from 1 to 9, the total might be odd or even.

Step Ahead   Mika is playing a game. He has to choose a number, double it, then add 3. He needs to get a total between 10 and 16.

Which numbers could he start with to get that total? _____

Show your thinking.

Computation Practice

★ To discover a fishy fact, write all the differences.
★ Then write each letter above its matching difference at the bottom of the page.

18 − 3 = ☐ **a**

31 − 2 = ☐ **i**

70 − 2 = ☐ **l**

9 − 2 = ☐ **h**

46 − 1 = ☐ **u**

16 − 3 = ☐ **n**

42 − 3 = ☐ **c**

56 − 2 = ☐ **d**

27 − 1 = ☐ **s**

8 − 3 = ☐ **q**

61 − 2 = ☐ **e**

51 − 3 = ☐ **t**

Some letters appear more than once.

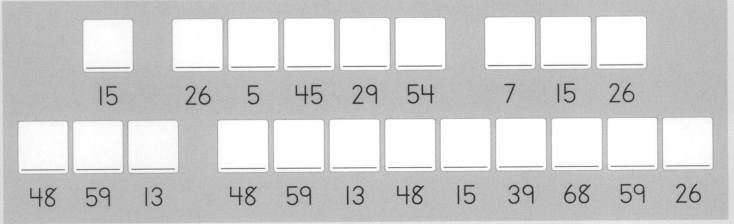

☐ ☐ ☐ ☐ ☐ ☐   ☐ ☐ ☐
15   26 5 45 29 54   7   15 26

☐ ☐ ☐   ☐ ☐ ☐ ☐ ☐ ☐ ☐ ☐ ☐
48 59 13   48 59 13 48 15 39 68 59 26

© ORIGO Education

Ongoing Practice

1. Compare the mass of each item. Then write **more** or **less** to complete each sentence.

a.

The sugar weighs _____ than the yogurt.

b.

The bread weighs _____ than the butter.

2. Write each time in words.

a.

9:30

_____

_____

b.

6:00

_____

_____

Preparing for Module 3

Write these numbers in order from **least** to **greatest**.

a.

| 11 | 33 | 18 | 25 |

____ ____ ____ ____

b.

| 28 | 54 | 43 | 31 |

____ ____ ____ ____

c.

| 78 | 62 | 57 | 73 |

____ ____ ____ ____

d.

| 12 | 60 | 17 | 49 |

____ ____ ____ ____

Step In

What doubles fact does this domino show?

What equation can you write to show this double?

```
┌──────────────────────────────────┐
│                                  │
│                                  │
│                                  │
└──────────────────────────────────┘
```

How can you use that doubles fact to figure out the total number of dots on this domino?

What equation can you write to match?

```
┌──────────────────────────────────┐
│                                  │
│                                  │
│                                  │
└──────────────────────────────────┘
```

What doubles fact would you use to figure out each of these?

$6 + 7 = \boxed{}$ $8 + 6 = \boxed{}$

Step Up

1. Write the doubles fact you would use to figure out each **double-plus-1** fact. Then complete the fact.

a.

I can use double $\boxed{}$. $3 + 4 = \boxed{}$

b.

I can use double $\boxed{}$. $7 + 8 = \boxed{}$

c.

I can use double $\boxed{}$. $8 + 9 = \boxed{}$

2. Write the doubles fact that helps. Then complete each **double-plus-2** fact.

a.

I can use double ☐. $5 + 7 =$ ☐

b.

I can use double ☐. $3 + 5 =$ ☐

c.

I can use double ☐. $7 + 9 =$ ☐

3. Write the total. Then write the **turnaround**.

a. $4 + 5 =$ ☐

☐ $+$ ☐ $=$ ☐

b. $4 + 6 =$ ☐

☐ $+$ ☐ $=$ ☐

c. $6 + 5 =$ ☐

☐ $+$ ☐ $=$ ☐

d. $8 + 7 =$ ☐

☐ $+$ ☐ $=$ ☐

e. $8 + 10 =$ ☐

☐ $+$ ☐ $=$ ☐

f. $10 + 9 =$ ☐

☐ $+$ ☐ $=$ ☐

Step Ahead

a. Write a doubles equation that has a total greater than 20.

☐ $+$ ☐ $=$ ☐

b. Then use this known total to write four near-doubles equations.

☐ $+$ ☐ $=$ ☐

☐ $+$ ☐ $=$ ☐

☐ $+$ ☐ $=$ ☐

☐ $+$ ☐ $=$ ☐

Step In What addition fact would you write to match each domino?

Circle the domino that shows 3 + 4.

How would you figure out the total?
What are some of the different strategies that you could use?

I know that double 3 is 6, so 3 + 4 is one more.

I would count on from four. That's 4...5, 6, 7.

What about the other dominoes?
What strategy could you use to figure out each total?

Share a word problem to match each domino.

Step Up I. Write each total. Then write **D** on the facts that you solved by thinking about a double.

a.
6 + 2 =

b.
7 + 7 =

c.
8 + 6 =

d.
8 + 9 =

e.
8 + 3 =

f.
5 + 2 =

2. Solve each problem. Show your thinking.

a. Lisa counts 8 stickers in her workbook. Deon has one more sticker than Lisa. How many stickers do they have in total?

☐_____ stickers

b. Jamal and Trina sold 13 tickets in total. Jamal sold 7 tickets. How many tickets did Trina sell?

☐_____ tickets

c. Hunter has 9 animal cards in his collection. He has 3 fewer cards than Megan. How many cards does Megan have?

☐_____ cards

d. Some friends are at the park. 5 more arrive. There are now 11 friends in total. How many were at the park before?

☐_____ friends

Step Ahead Write a word problem that you could solve by thinking about a doubles fact.

Think and Solve Write these numbers in the story below so that it makes sense. Each number can be used only once.

| 6 | 12 | 10 | 5 |

Daniel is the oldest. He is almost _____ years old.

Jayden is half Daniel's age. He is only _____ .

Jude is _____ years old and in grade _____ .

Words at Work Write an addition word problem that you would solve by using the doubles strategy. You can use words from the list to help.

| add |
| number |
| how many |
| total |
| one more |
| double |
| two more |

Ongoing Practice

1. Write the number of cubes. Then color the ◯ beside the words that best describe the mass of the toy.

a.

◯ more than _____ cubes

◯ fewer than _____ cubes

◯ balances _____ cubes

b.

◯ more than _____ cubes

◯ fewer than _____ cubes

◯ balances _____ cubes

2. Write the doubles fact that helps. Then complete each **near-double** fact.

a.

I can use double ⬜.

$5 + 6 =$ ⬜

b.

I can use double ⬜.

$8 + 6 =$ ⬜

Preparing for Module 3

Draw more counters. Then write the numbers to match.

a. Draw 4 more.

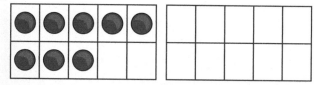

see ➡ ⬜ + ⬜

think ➡ ⬜ + ⬜

b. Draw 6 more.

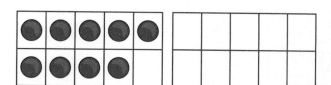

see ➡ ⬜ + ⬜

think ➡ ⬜ + ⬜

Step In | What number does this picture of blocks show?

How do you know?

How could you write the number on this expander?

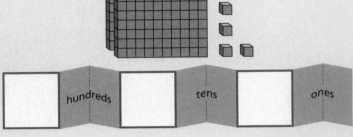

hundreds   tens   ones

What does the zero mean?
Do you say the value of the tens when you read the number?

Two hundred six. You don't say the zero when you read the number out loud.

What does the zero mean in each of these numbers?

20	105	60	140	507	230

Step Up | **1.** Color blocks to match the number on the expander.

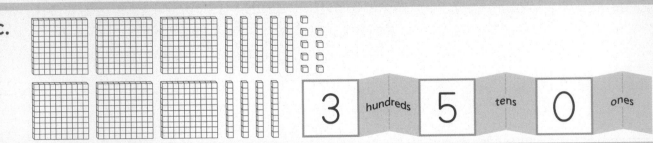

a.

5 hundreds   0 tens   2 ones

b.

6 hundreds   0 tens   9 ones

c.

3 hundreds   5 tens   0 ones

2. Look at the blocks. Write the matching number on the expanders.

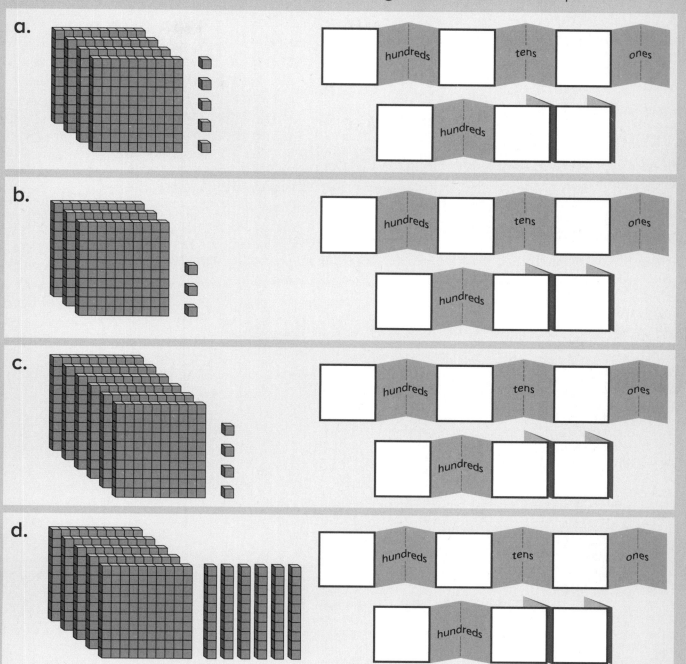

a. [ ] hundreds [ ] tens [ ] ones

[ ] hundreds [ ] [ ]

b. [ ] hundreds [ ] tens [ ] ones

[ ] hundreds [ ] [ ]

c. [ ] hundreds [ ] tens [ ] ones

[ ] hundreds [ ] [ ]

d. [ ] hundreds [ ] tens [ ] ones

[ ] hundreds [ ] [ ]

Step Ahead

Use **only** these digits. Write all the different two-digit numerals **and** three-digit numerals that you can. Digits can be used more than once.

⓪ ① ②

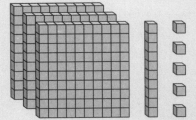

Step In

How do you say the number shown by the blocks in this picture?

Three hundred fifteen. You say the tens and ones together.

How could you write the number on this expander?

hundreds

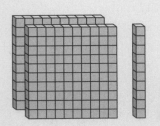

How do you say the total number shown by these blocks?

Step Up

I. Color blocks to match the number on the expander.

a.

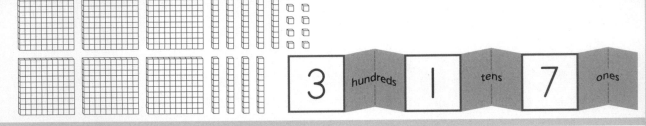

3 hundreds | 1 tens | 7 ones

b.

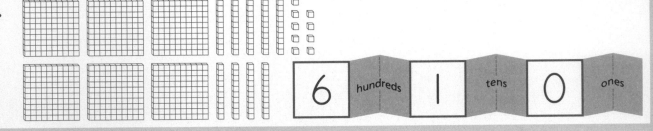

6 hundreds | 1 tens | 0 ones

c.

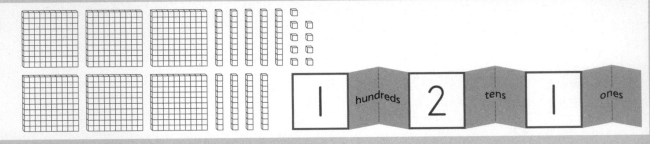

1 hundreds | 2 tens | 1 ones

© ORIGO Education

2. Look at the blocks. Write the matching number on the expanders.

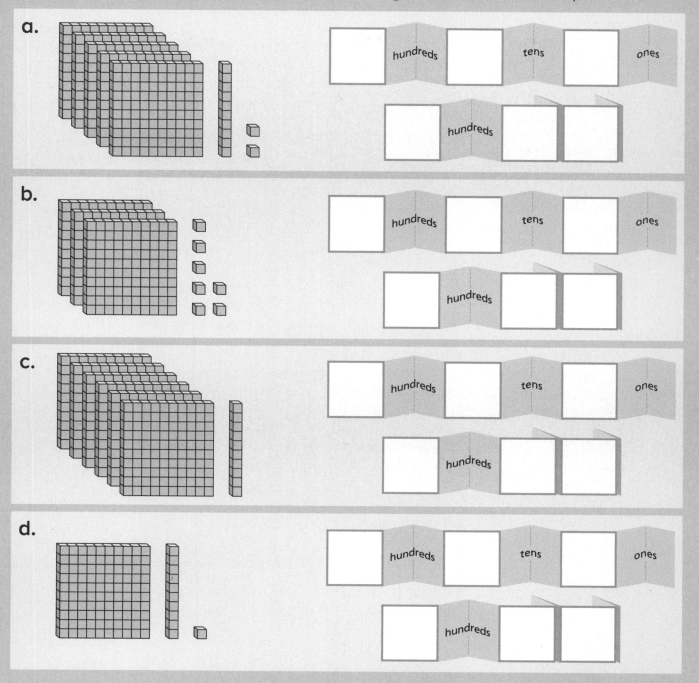

a.

	hundreds		tens		ones

	hundreds		

b.

	hundreds		tens		ones

	hundreds		

c.

	hundreds		tens		ones

	hundreds		

d.

	hundreds		tens		ones

	hundreds		

Step Ahead

Figure out the number shown by these blocks.
Write the number on the expander.

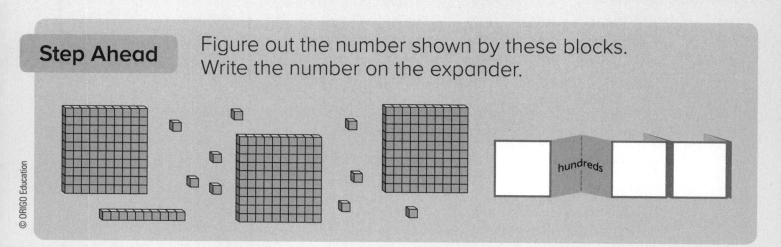

	hundreds		

Maintaining concepts and skills

Computation Practice

★ Complete the equations as fast as you can.

start

18 - 9 = ____

4 - 3 = ____

7 - 1 = ____

9 - 7 = ____

6 - 2 = ____

7 - 7 = ____

8 - 4 = ____

12 - 3 = ____

8 - 2 = ____

3 - 1 = ____

15 - 8 = ____

5 - 1 = ____

9 - 5 = ____

13 - 7 = ____

9 - 3 = ____

12 - 5 = ____

17 - 8 = ____

10 - 2 = ____

11 - 2 = ____

12 - 6 = ____

finish

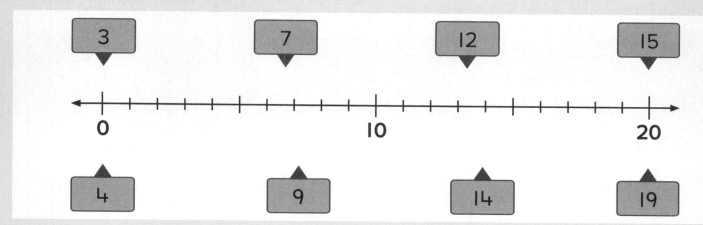
Ongoing Practice

1. Draw a line from each number to its position on the number line.

2. Look at the blocks. Write the matching number on the expanders.

a.

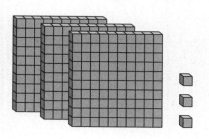

FROM 2.3.1

hundreds   tens   ones

hundreds

b.

hundreds   tens   ones

hundreds

Preparing for Module 4

Write the answers. Draw jumps on the number track to help you.

| 1 | 2 | 3 | 4 | 5 | 6 | 7 | 8 | 9 | 10 |

a. 4 − 1 =

b. 10 − 2 =

c. 7 − 2 =

Step In

What number is shown by this picture of blocks?

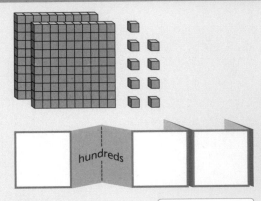

How do you know?

Write the number on the expander.

How would you write the number without the expander?
Do you still need to write the zero to describe the tens? Why?

How would you write the number in words?

_____ hundred _____

Step Up

I. Look at the blocks. Write the matching number on the expanders.

a.
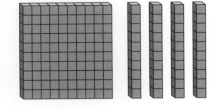
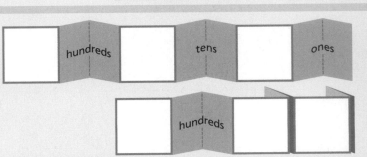

hundreds   tens   ones

hundreds

b.
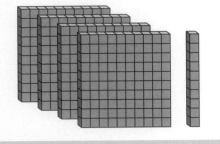
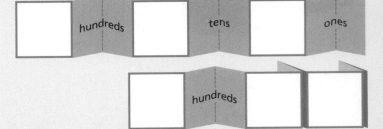

hundreds   tens   ones

hundreds

c.
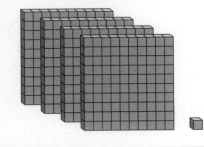

hundreds   tens   ones

hundreds

2. Look at the expander. Write the matching number, and then the number name.

a.

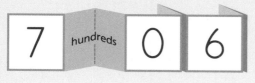

_____ hundred _____

b.

_____ hundred _____

c.

_____ hundred _____

d.

_____ hundred _____

Step Ahead   Write a number to match each description.

a. four hundreds
zero tens
three ones

b. eight hundreds
four ones
one ten

c. seven tens
nine ones
two hundreds

Step In

What number is shown by each type of block in this picture?

Carter writes this to show the value of each type of block.

$$200 + 40 + 5$$

Carter has written the number in **expanded form**.

Read the number on the expander.

What value does each digit represent?

| 4 | hundreds | 0 | 5 |

Complete the equation to show the number written in expanded form.

$$405 = \boxed{} + \boxed{} + \boxed{}$$

Step Up

I. Look at the blocks. Write the matching number on the expander. Then write the number in expanded form.

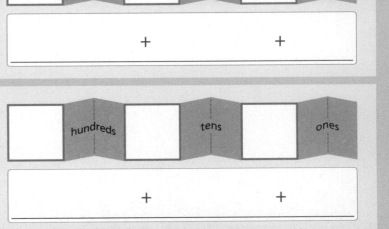

a.

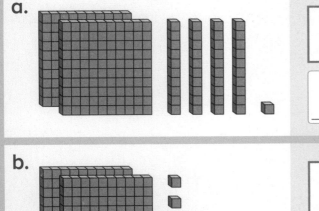

| 2 | hundreds | 4 | tens | 1 | ones |

_____ + _____ + _____

b.

| | hundreds | | tens | | ones |

_____ + _____ + _____

2. Write each number in expanded form.

a.
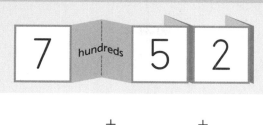

_____ + _____ + _____

b.
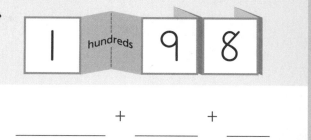

_____ + _____ + _____

c.
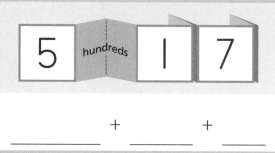

_____ + _____ + _____

d.
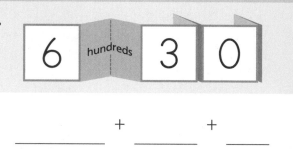

_____ + _____ + _____

3. Write each number in expanded form.

a.
428 = [＿＿＿] + [＿＿＿] + [＿＿＿]

b.
299 = [＿＿＿] + [＿＿＿] + [＿＿＿]

c.
912 = [＿＿＿] + [＿＿＿] + [＿＿＿]

d.
680 = [＿＿＿] + [＿＿＿] + [＿＿＿]

Step Ahead — On each expander, write the number that has been expanded.

a. 500 + 10 + 4
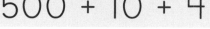

b. 800 + 90

c. 600 + 2

d. 100 + 20 + 6

Think and Solve Same shapes weigh the same.
Write the missing value inside each shape.

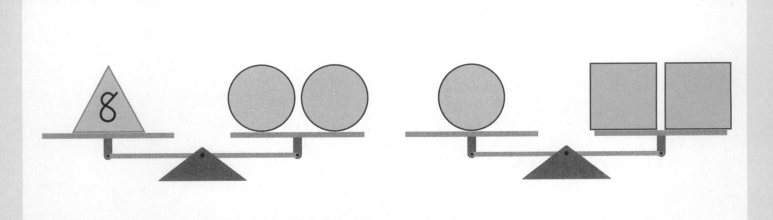

Circle the shape that is the heaviest.

Words at Work
Write about the different ways to show the number 257. You can use words from the list to help.

| expander |
| expanded form |
| hundreds |
| tens |
| ones |
| blocks |
| words |
| numeral |

I. For each number, write the **ten** that is closest.
You can use the number line to help.

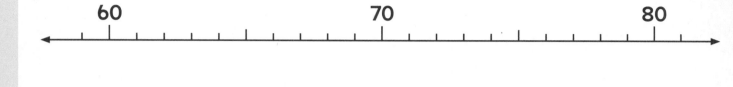

60   70   80

a.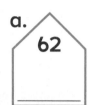
62
____

b.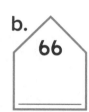
66
____

c.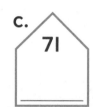
71
____

d.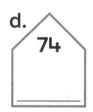
74
____

e.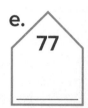
77
____

2. Look at the blocks. Write the matching number on the expanders.

a.
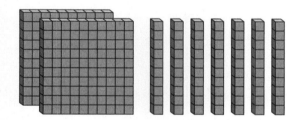
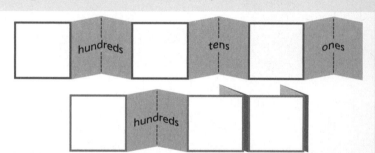

hundreds   tens   ones

hundreds

b.
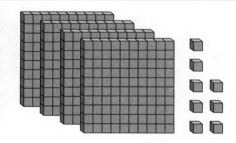
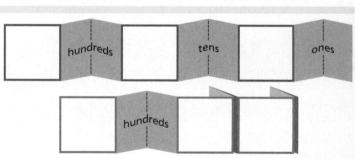

hundreds   tens   ones

hundreds

Preparing for Module 4

Draw dots to figure out the missing part.
Then complete the facts to match.

a. 8 dots in total

8 – 3 = ☐

think

3 + ☐ = 8

b. 9 dots in total

9 – 2 = ☐

think

2 + ☐ = 9

Step In   This number line shows steps of 100 from zero.

Start at zero and count on by 100s.
Write the numbers you say below the marks on the number line.

0

What number did you write at the last mark on the number line?
What do you know about that number?

Are there more than or fewer than 1,000 seats in your school hall?

Are there more than or fewer than 1,000 students in your school?

What other numbers could you label on the number line? How do you know?

The number line above is useful for showing numbers such as 400 or 750. The same number line can be broken into smaller parts to show numbers such as 273 or 618.

What numbers could you show on this number line?

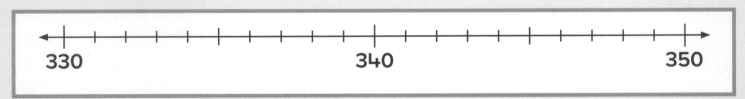

330   340   350

Step Up   I.   Look carefully at the number line. Then write the correct number below each mark.

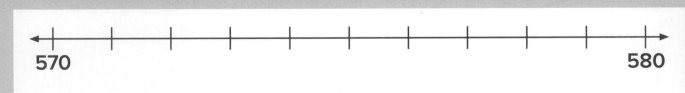

570   580

Write the number that should be in the position shown by each arrow.

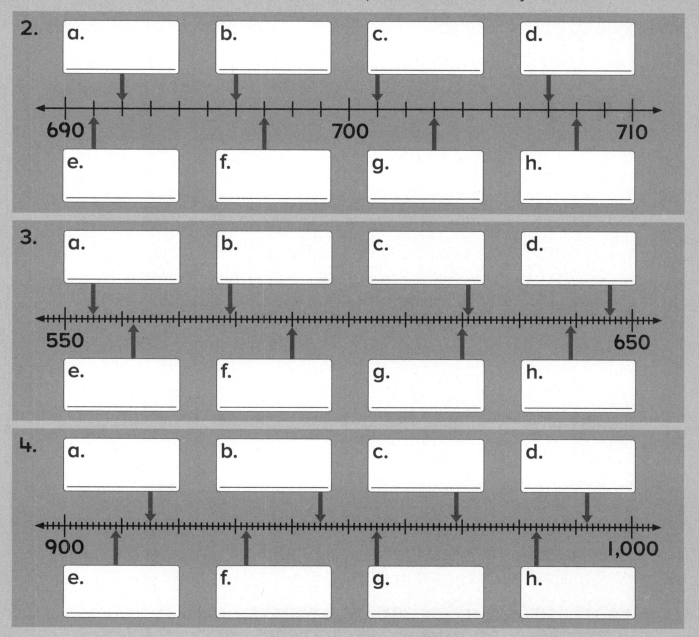

2.
a. _____
b. _____
c. _____
d. _____

690   700   710

e. _____
f. _____
g. _____
h. _____

3.
a. _____
b. _____
c. _____
d. _____

550   650

e. _____
f. _____
g. _____
h. _____

4.
a. _____
b. _____
c. _____
d. _____

900   1,000

e. _____
f. _____
g. _____
h. _____

Step Ahead   Write the number that each arrow **could** be pointing to.

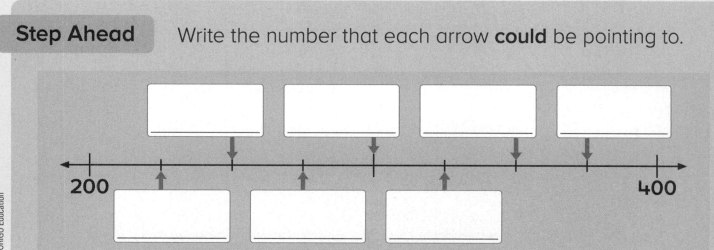

200   400

Step In   The wingspan of an airplane is the distance between the tips of its wings.

Look at the wingspans of these airplanes.

Plane	Wingspan
A	214 feet
B	199 feet
C	147 feet
D	156 feet

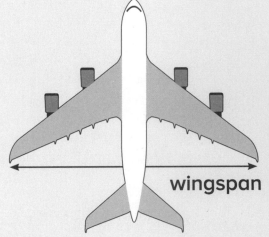

wingspan

Which plane has the longest wingspan? How did you figure it out?
Which place in the numbers did you look at first? Why?

Look at the wingspan of Plane D.

You could use this place-value chart to show 156.
What do the abbreviations H, T, and O mean?

H	T	O
1	5	6

Step Up   1. Compare the numbers in the place-value charts. Circle the words that are true.

a.

H	T	O
5	7	2

is greater than

is less than

H	T	O
4	8	9

b.

H	T	O
3	1	6

is greater than

is less than

H	T	O
3	0	6

2. Write **is greater than** or **is less than** to make true statements.

a. 478 _____Less_____ _____Grater_____ 485

b. 374 _____Bigh_____ _____Less_____ 347

c. 126 _____Less_____ _____Bigh_____ 129

d. 531 _____Bigr_____ _____Less_____ 530

3. Write **<**, **=**, or **>** to describe how the numbers compare.

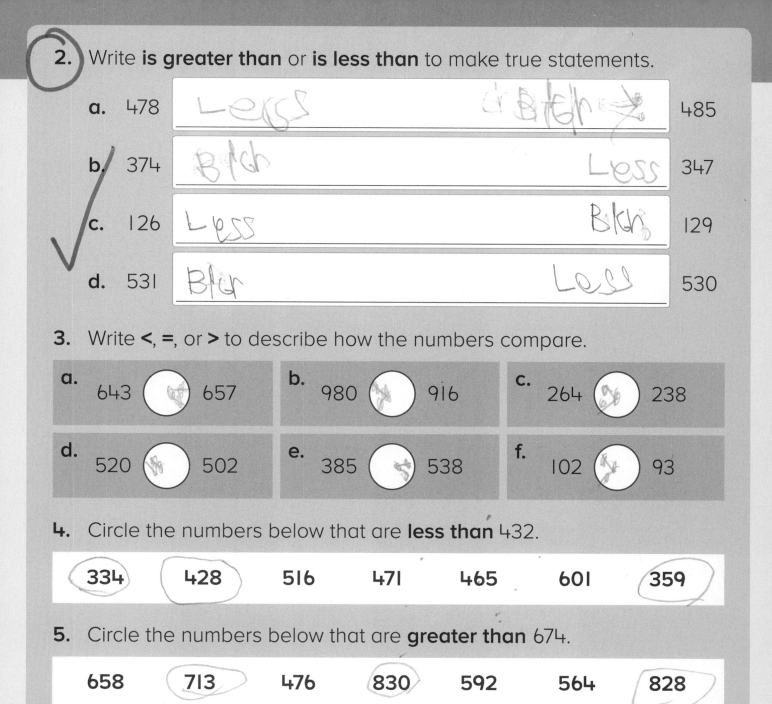

a. 643 ◯ 657

b. 980 ◯ 916

c. 264 ◯ 238

d. 520 ◯ 502

e. 385 ◯ 538

f. 102 ◯ 93

4. Circle the numbers below that are **less than** 432.

(334)   (428)   516   471   465   601   (359)

5. Circle the numbers below that are **greater than** 674.

658   (713)   476   (830)   592   564   (828)

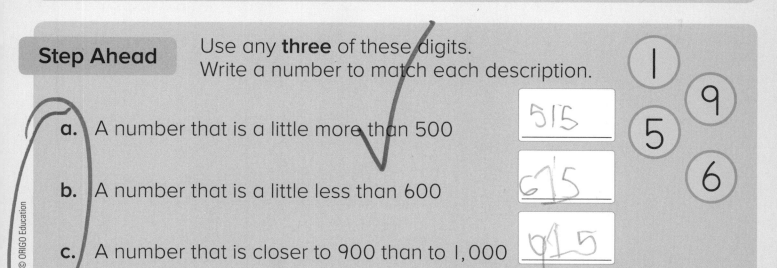

Step Ahead

Use any **three** of these digits.
Write a number to match each description.

① ⑨ ⑤ ⑥

a. A number that is a little more than 500   515

b. A number that is a little less than 600   675

c. A number that is closer to 900 than to 1,000   915

Computation Practice   **What pet is hiding in the puzzle?**

★ Write all the totals.
★ Then find the totals in the picture below and color these parts orange.
★ Color the other parts blue.

25 + 1 = ☐

7 + 2 = ☐

38 + 3 = ☐

3 + 59 = ☐

1 + 18 = ☐

2 + 29 = ☐

6 + 1 = ☐

46 + 3 = ☐

53 + 1 = ☐

2 + 69 = ☐

37 + 2 = ☐

9 + 1 = ☐

19 + 3 = ☐

3 + 27 = ☐

49 + 2 = ☐

47 + 1 = ☐

1 + 34 = ☐

2 + 16 = ☐

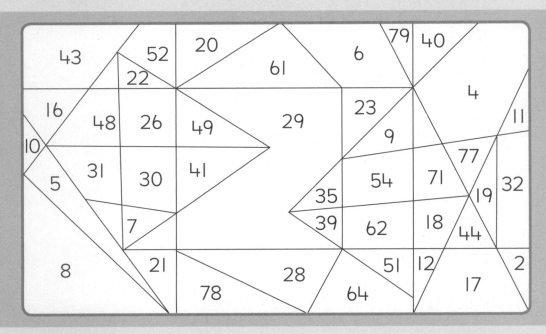

1. Write each time in words.

a.

b.

FROM 2.2.8

2. Write the number that should be in the position shown by each arrow.

a.

b.

c.

d.

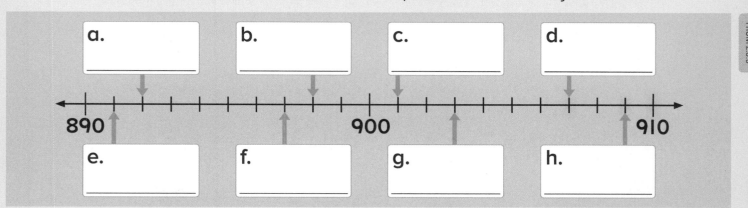

e.

f.

g.

h.

FROM 2.3.5

Preparing for Module 4

Color the animals to show two groups.
Then write an addition fact and subtraction fact to match each picture.

a.

☐ + ☐ = ☐

☐ − ☐ = ☐

b.

☐ + ☐ = ☐

☐ − ☐ = ☐

Step In Look at each game score card.

GAME 1	POINTS
Riku	452
William	524
Wendell	254

GAME 2	POINTS
Alicia	368
Morgan	386
Grace	380

Who won each game? How do you know?

What place in the numbers did you look at first?

Which place did you look at next?

Use any three of these digits.

Write the greatest three-digit number that is possible.

How did you decide what number to write?

Write two different three-digit numbers using any of the digits above.

Look at the three numbers you wrote.
Rewrite them in order from **least** to **greatest**.

How did you figure out the order?

Step Up 1. For each score card, write the scores for the 1st, 2nd, and 3rd places. The team with the greatest score wins.

a.

Bears	379
Eels	385
Hawks	368

1st	2nd	3rd

b.

Rangers	223
Kings	218
Rockers	231

1st	2nd	3rd

2. Write the scores for the 1st, 2nd, 3rd, and last places. The team with the greatest score wins.

a.

Eagles	381
Tigers	308
Falcons	380
Sharks	318

1st	2nd	3rd	Last

b.

Seals	499
Crocs	419
Stingrays	491
Snakes	409

1st	2nd	3rd	Last

c.

Bulls	212
Roosters	221
Stallions	210
Rams	220

1st	2nd	3rd	Last

d.

Smashers	890
Strikers	809
Twisters	980
Chargers	819

1st	2nd	3rd	Last

e.

Breakers	459
Thrashers	495
Crackers	517
Flyers	509

1st	2nd	3rd	Last

f.

Comets	179
Blasters	212
Rockets	197
Scorchers	206

1st	2nd	3rd	Last

Step Ahead

a. Use only these digits. Write the **six** different three-digit numbers that are possible.

  5 9 8

b. Write your numbers in order from **greatest** to **least**.

Step In This number chart starts at 401 and ends at 500.

What numbers are covered?
How do you know?

I counted by tens to figure out the missing numbers.

Read this number puzzle.

I am between 400 and 450. My number has 2 tens. You say my number when you start at 400 and count by 10s. **?**

Color the number chart to show the answer.

401	402	403	404	405	406	407	408	409	410
411	412	413	414	415	416	417	418	419	420
421	422	423	424	425	426	427	428	429	430
431	432	433	434	435	436	437	438	439	440
441	442	443	444	445	446	447	448	449	450
451				455	456	457	458	459	460
46				66	467	468	469	470
47			76	477	478	479	480
		486	487	488	489	490
	496	497	498	499	500

Step Up 1. Write the number that is **10 greater** or **10 less**.

10 less						
	470	424	162	856	515	319
10 greater						

2. Write the number that is **100 greater** or **100 less**.

100 less						
	432	480	283	389	612	109
100 greater						

3. Solve these number puzzles.

701	702	703	704	705	706	707	708	709	710
711	712	713	714	715	716	717	718	719	720
721	722	723	724	725	726	727	728	729	730
731	732	733	734	735		37	738	739	740
741	742	743	744	74					750
751	752	753	754						
761	762	763	76						70
771	772	773							780
781	782	783	784					9	790
791	792	793	794	795	796			799	800

a. I am between 750 and 800. My number has 4 ones. The digits in my tens and hundreds places are the same.

b. I am less than 750. You say my number if you start at 712 and count by 10s. I have the same number of tens and ones.

c. I am greater than 730. My number has 0 ones. The digits in my hundreds and tens places are the same.

d. I am between 750 and 800. My number has 8 tens. You say my number if you start at 758 and count by 10s.

4. Try to solve these puzzles without a number chart.

a. I am between 200 and 250. You say my number when you start at 150 and count by 10s. The digits in my tens and hundreds places are the same.

b. My number is greater than 300 but less than 400. It has 0 tens. You say my number if you start at 290 and count by 5s.

Step Ahead Think of a number that is less than 500. Then write three clues about your number.

Think and Solve These beads make a chain. Jane repeats these beads to make some more chains.

a. She uses 8 ◯ and ⬚ ■.   b. She makes ⬚ chains.

c. She will need ⬚ ◯ if she uses 30 ■.

Words at Work   a. Write a three-digit number.

⬚

b. Write three clues for your number.
You can use words from the list to help you.

| steps of |
| greater than |
| hundreds |
| tens |
| ones |
| count |
| fewer |

© ORIGO Education

1. Write each time in words.

FROM 2.2.8

a.

_____

_____

b.

_____

_____

c.

_____

_____

d.

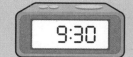
9:30

_____

_____

e.

11:00

_____

_____

f.

6:30

_____

_____

2. **a.** Use only these digits. Write **all** the different three-digit numbers that are possible.

6 5 4

FROM 2.3.7

b. Write your numbers in order from **greatest** to **least**.

Preparing for Module 4

Color the objects that are about the same length as this cube train.

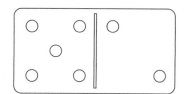

Step In   Look at this ten-frame and counters.

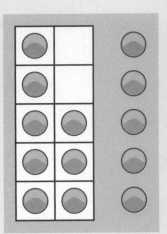

How could you figure out the total number
of counters without counting by ones?

Ten is easy to work with,
so I would add 2 then add
3 more which is 13.

What other numbers could you add in this way?

Step Up   1.   Complete these equations.

a.
$$9 + 1 + 4 = \boxed{}$$

b.
$$8 + 2 + 1 = \boxed{}$$

c.
$$7 + 3 + 4 = \boxed{}$$

d.
$$2 + 8 + 5 = \boxed{}$$

e.
$$1 + 9 + 5 = \boxed{}$$

f.
$$2 + 8 + 7 = \boxed{}$$

2.   Draw more counters to figure out the total. Then write the total.
Remember to fill one ten-frame first.

a.
$$9 + 5 = \boxed{}$$

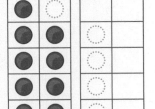

b.
$$8 + 6 = \boxed{}$$

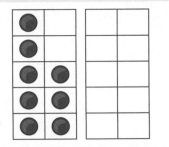

c.
$$7 + 5 = \boxed{}$$

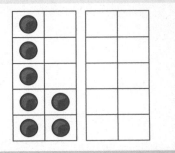

3. Use the make-ten strategy to figure out the total. Then write two facts to match.

a.

domino: 9 | 6 dots

___ + ___ = ___

___ + ___ = ___

b.

domino: 8 | 4 dots

___ + ___ = ___

___ + ___ = ___

c.

domino: 4 dots | 9

___ + ___ = ___

___ + ___ = ___

d.

domino: 7 | 6 dots

___ + ___ = ___

___ + ___ = ___

e.

domino: 8 | 9 dots

___ + ___ = ___

___ + ___ = ___

f.

domino: 3 | 6 dots

___ + ___ = ___

___ + ___ = ___

4. Figure out the total. Then write the turnaround fact.

a. $7 + 4 =$ ☐

☐ + ☐ = ☐

b. $9 + 7 =$ ☐

☐ + ☐ = ☐

c. $7 + 8 =$ ☐

☐ + ☐ = ☐

Step Ahead   Complete these equations.

a. $18 + 2 + 1 =$ ☐

b. $1 + 19 + 5 =$ ☐

c. $3 + 17 +$ ☐ $= 24$

d. $1 + 19 + 3 =$ ☐

e. $17 + 3 + 6 =$ ☐

f. $18 +$ ☐ $+ 3 = 23$

Step In

How could you figure out the total cost of the hat and sunscreen?

$9

$5

Sunscreen

You could start at 9 and count by ones.

Jie uses a ten-frame to figure out the total.

How does the ten-frame help Jie figure out the total?

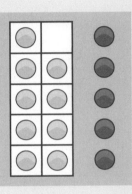

I can fill the frame to make a ten. It's much easier to figure out 10 + 4 than 9 + 5.

What thinking would you use to figure out 8 + 6?

Step Up

I. Write the make-ten equation that you would use to figure out each total.

a.

see ▶ 9 + 3

think ▶ ☐ + ☐ = ☐

b.

see ▶ 8 + 5

think ▶ ☐ + ☐ = ☐

c.

see ▶ 8 + 3

think ▶ ☐ + ☐ = ☐

d.

see ▶ 9 + 6

think ▶ ☐ + ☐ = ☐

2. Using the prices above, figure out the total cost of the items below.

a.

$\$$___ + $\$$___ = $\$$_____

b.

$\$$___ + $\$$___ = $\$$_____

c.

$\$$___ + $\$$___ = $\$$_____

d.

$\$$___ + $\$$___ = $\$$_____

Step Ahead Extend the make-ten strategy to figure out 19 + 7.

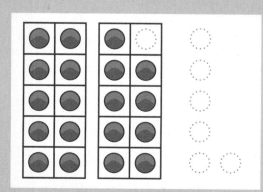

see → | 19 | + | 7 |

think → ___ + ___ = ___

Computation Practice   What creature is hiding in the puzzle?

★ Write the total for each number fact.
★ Find each total in the picture and color the part yellow.
★ Color the remaining parts green.

8 + 2 = ☐	2 + 5 = ☐	8 + 7 = ☐
3 + 1 = ☐	7 + 9 = ☐	4 + 2 = ☐
4 + 9 = ☐	5 + 4 = ☐	9 + 5 = ☐
6 + 5 = ☐	1 + 2 = ☐	3 + 2 = ☐
9 + 8 = ☐	5 + 7 = ☐	7 + 1 = ☐

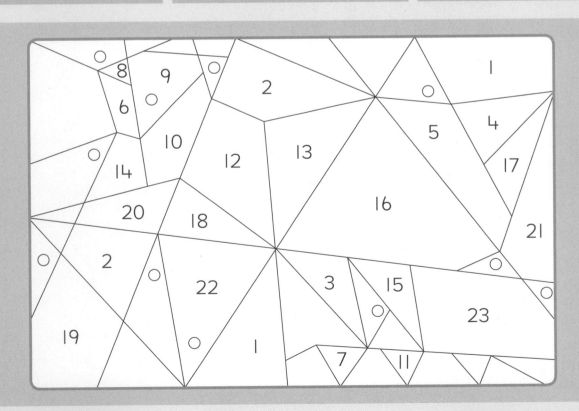

Ongoing Practice

1. Color the ⬭ beside four statements that describe this object.

○ It can roll.

○ It can stack.

○ It has all flat surfaces.

○ It cannot roll.

○ It has all curved surfaces.

○ It has 5 surfaces.

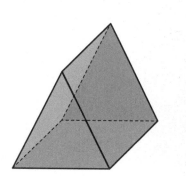

2. Draw more counters to figure out the total. Then write the total. Remember to fill one ten-frame first.

a.

9 + 4 = ☐

b.

8 + 5 = ☐

c.

7 + 6 = ☐

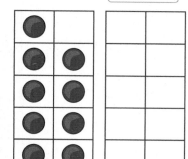

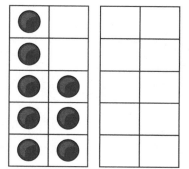

Preparing for Module 4

Look at the ant trail. Write how many ants long each pencil is.

_____ ants long

_____ ants long

_____ ants long

Step In

What addition fact would you write to match this domino?

How would you figure out the total number of dots? What strategy could you use?

I would use the make-ten strategy. See 9 + 7 and think 10 + 6.

Counting on is too slow. I would use a double.

Circle the domino that shows an addition fact that you would solve by counting on.

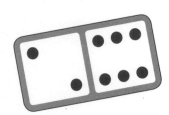 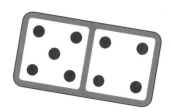 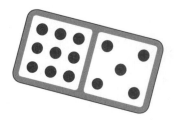

What other addition facts would you solve by using the count-on strategy?

Step Up

1. Write each total. Then write **C**, **D**, or **M** in each circle to show the strategy you used to figure out the total.

a. ◯ 8 + 3 = ▢

b. ◯ 6 + 5 = ▢

Ⓒ count-on

Ⓓ doubles

Ⓜ make-ten

c. ◯ 1 + 7 = ▢

d. ◯ 9 + 9 = ▢

e. ◯ 0 + 4 = ▢

f. ◯ 9 + 3 = ▢

g. ◯ 7 + 8 = ▢

2. Solve each problem. Show your thinking.

a. Some children are in the pool. 5 more children jump in. There are now 12 children in the pool. How many were in the pool before?

 children

b. There are only 8 people in the cinema. Some more people arrive. There are now 17 people. How many people just arrived?

_____ people

c. John has read 4 pages of his book. Paige has read 9 more pages than John but 2 fewer than Susan. How many pages has Susan read?

_____ pages

d. There are 16 dancers in the class. There are two groups and one group has 2 more dancers than the other. How many are in each group?

 dancers dancers

Step Ahead   Read the problem. Then color the card to show the thinking you would use to solve the problem.

Today, Karen made 7 calls on her cell phone. She made 4 fewer calls than the day before. How many calls did she make the day before?

$7 - 4 = \boxed{}$

$4 + \boxed{} = 7$

$7 + 4 = \boxed{}$

$7 - \boxed{} = 4$

Step In   What do you notice about this number puzzle?

How would you figure out the number that is missing?

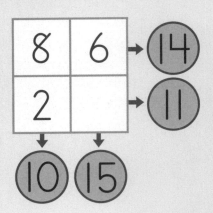

The numbers in the circles tell the total of each column or row. I could figure out the missing number by thinking 2 + __ = 11 or 6 + __ = 15.

How would you figure out the numbers that are missing in this puzzle?

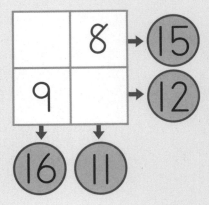

Step Up   1.   Write the missing numbers to complete each equation.

a. $8 + 3 = \boxed{}$

b. $\boxed{} + 6 = 11$

c. $3 + \boxed{} = 12$

d. $\boxed{} = 9 + 9$

e. $17 = \boxed{} + 8$

f. $\boxed{} + 8 = 14$

g. $10 = 7 + \boxed{}$

h. $9 = \boxed{} + 0$

i. $6 + 6 = \boxed{}$

j. $\boxed{} + \boxed{} = 15$

k. $10 = 2 + \boxed{}$

l. $13 = \boxed{} + \boxed{}$

2. Add the two numbers across each row and write the total in the matching circle. Then add the two numbers down each column and write the total in the matching circle.

a.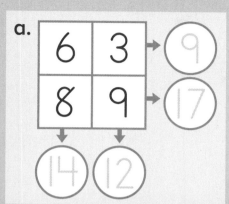

b.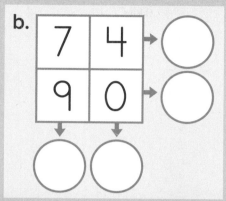

c.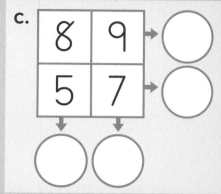

3. Write the missing numbers to complete these puzzles.

a.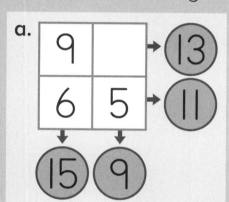

b.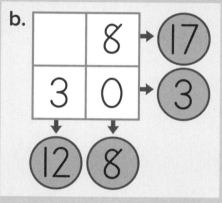

c.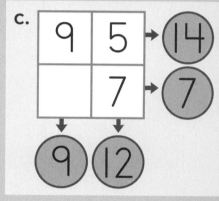

d.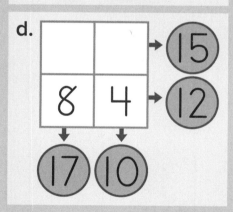

e.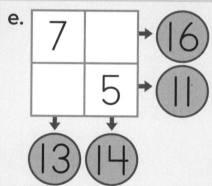

f.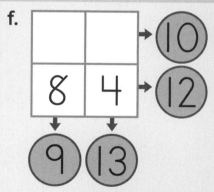

Step Ahead

Write the three missing numbers to complete this puzzle.

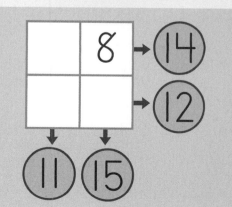

Think and Solve Follow the arrows and figure out the number pattern.

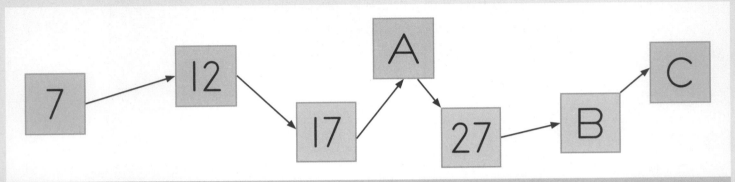

Write the missing numbers.

A = ☐   B = ☐   C = ☐

Words at Work Choose and write words from the list to complete these sentences. Each word is used only once.

a. When you say a three-digit number, you say

the _____ and ones together.

b.

A number can be written in expanded _____.

c.

406 has four hundreds, _____ tens, and six ones.

d.

An _____ is used to show the value of each digit in a number.

e. When you compare two three-digit numbers, you look at the

digit in the _____ place first.

hundreds
form
zero
expander
tens

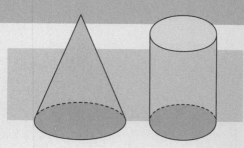

Ongoing Practice

1. Look at these pictures.

How are the objects the same?

2. Solve each problem. Show your thinking.

a. Ramon buys 12 stickers. 5 stickers show birds and the rest show cars. How many car stickers did Ramon buy?	b. Liam caught 4 fish. Julia caught 2 more fish than Liam. How many fish did Julia catch?
☐ car stickers	☐ fish

Preparing for Module 4

Look at the cube train. Draw a pencil that is between 3 and 5 cubes long.

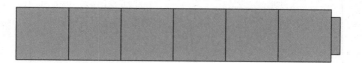

Step In   **What subtraction story could you say about this picture?**

Which numbers are the parts in your story?

What number is the total in your story?

What subtraction story could you say about these mice?

Which numbers are the parts in your story?

What number is the total in your story?

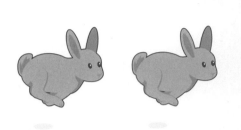

What subtraction equations could you write for each story?

How do you know what to write?

Step Up   **I.**   Write numbers to match the picture.
Then complete the equation.

There were [ ] apples on the bench.

[ ] apples were eaten.

There are [ ] whole apples left.

[ ] − [ ] = [ ]

2. Solve each problem. Show your thinking.

a. Natalie has 8 trading cards. She gives her brother 3 of them. How many cards does Natalie have left?

☐ cards

b. There are 7 shirts. 3 have short sleeves and the rest have long sleeves. How many have long sleeves?

☐ shirts

c. 5 beads are in a box. 2 beads are on the table. How many more beads are in the box than on the table?

☐ beads

d. Some books are on a shelf. Dwane takes 4 of the books. One book is left. How many books are there in total?

☐ books

Step Ahead

Gloria has $9. Which **two** toys can she buy so that she has $5 left?

$2 $4 $3 $2

☐ and ☐

© ORIGO Education

Step In   There are 11 books on a shelf.

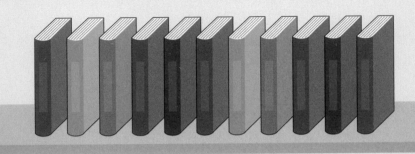

If Terri takes three books off the shelf, how many will be left?

I can count back to figure out the answer.

Start at 11... one less is 10...one less is 9... one less is 8... so there will be 8 books left.

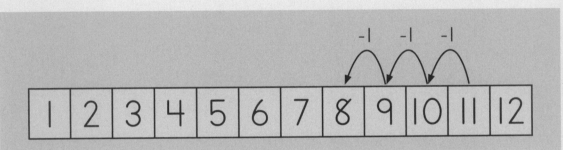

Instead of counting back by ones, what other jumps could you make?

Step Up   1.   Draw jumps on the number track to match each equation.

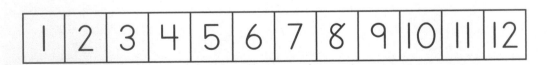

a.
6 − 2 = 4

b.
9 − 1 = 8

c.
12 − 2 = 10

© ORIGO Education

2. Write an equation to match what is shown on each number track.

a.

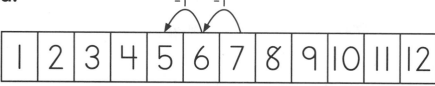

☐ − ☐ = ☐

b.

☐ − ☐ = ☐

c.

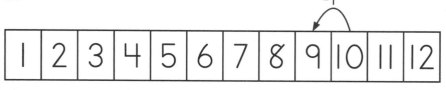

☐ − ☐ = ☐

3. Complete each equation. You can use the number track to help you.

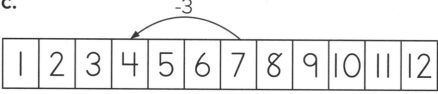

a. 5 − 1 = ☐

b. 8 − 3 = ☐

c. 11 − 2 = ☐

Step Ahead

Write the missing numbers to complete true equations going down and across.

	4		6	−		=	2
	−		+		−		−
	1					+		=	2
	=		=		=		=
☐	+	3	=	8		4		

Computation Practice

What is black and white and makes a really loud noise?

★ Write the differences. Then write each letter above its matching difference below.

$47 - 10 =$ ___ **i**	$54 - 20 =$ ___ **h**	$33 - 10 =$ ___ **a**
$68 - 20 =$ ___ **s**	$71 - 30 =$ ___ **l**	$85 - 10 =$ ___ **g**
$49 - 20 =$ ___ **e**	$37 - 10 =$ ___ **n**	$62 - 30 =$ ___ **t**
$59 - 20 =$ ___ **y**	$75 - 20 =$ ___ **u**	$94 - 30 =$ ___ **r**
$80 - 10 =$ ___ **p**	$41 - 10 =$ ___ **m**	$58 - 30 =$ ___ **d**

Some letters are used more than once.

23	70	29	27	75	55	37	27

70	41	23	39	37	27	75	32	34	29

28	64	55	31	48

1. Color blocks to match the number on the expander.

| 3 | hundreds | 1 | tens | 8 | ones |

2. Write numbers to match the picture. Then complete the equation.

a.

There are ☐ birds.

☐ birds are flying away.

There are ☐ birds left on the fence.

☐ − ☐ = ☐

Preparing for Module 5   Write the totals. Use the number chart to help.

a. $52 + 1 = $ ☐

b. $47 + 10 = $ ☐

c. $68 + 2 = $ ☐

41	42	43	44	45	46	47	48	49	50
51	52	53	54	55	56	57	58	59	60
61	62	63	64	65	66	67	68	69	70

Step In

Lillian has nine toy animals.

Seven are farm animals and the rest are dinosaurs. How many toys are dinosaurs?

What addition equation can you write to match the story?

What subtraction equation can you write?

I could write 7 + ? = 9 to show it as addition.
I could write 9 – ? = 7 or 9 – 7 = ? to show it as subtraction.
The unknown number is the same for all the equations.

The card on the right shows the story about Lillian's toys in a different way.

The number at the bottom shows the total number of toys.

Write the number missing at the top.

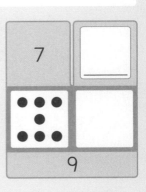

Step Up

1. Write the missing number and draw the matching dots on each card. Then complete the addition facts.

a.

5	3

8

5 + ☐ = 8

b.

☐	5

6

☐ + 5 = 6

c.

8	☐

10

8 + ☐ = 10

2. Figure out how many dots are covered.
Then write the matching equations.

a. **11** dots in total

☐ + ☐ = ☐

☐ − ☐ = ☐

b. **7** dots in total

☐ + ☐ = ☐

☐ − ☐ = ☐

c. **9** dots in total

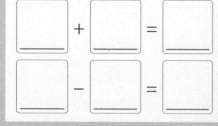

☐ + ☐ = ☐

☐ − ☐ = ☐

d. **8** dots in total

☐ + ☐ = ☐

☐ − ☐ = ☐

e. **5** dots in total

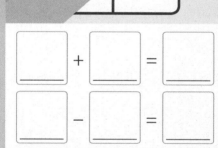

☐ + ☐ = ☐

☐ − ☐ = ☐

f. **10** dots in total

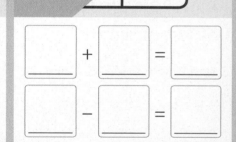

☐ + ☐ = ☐

☐ − ☐ = ☐

Step Ahead   Solve this problem. Show your thinking on page 156.

Mom gave Ben some money each afternoon. On Monday,
she gave him one nickel. On Tuesday, he got 2 nickels.
On Wednesday, he got 3. On Thursday, he got 4.

Every afternoon after Ben was given the nickels, he gave his little
brother one of them. Ben kept the rest.

How many nickels in total did Ben keep?

☐ nickels

© ORIGO Education

Step In

Reece went to the store with ten coins in his pocket.

Seven of them were quarters and the rest were pennies. How many pennies did he have?

What information in the story helps you figure out the answer? What information does not help?

What addition facts could you write to match the story?

What subtraction facts could you write to match the story?

Step Up

1. Write two subtraction facts to match each domino.

a. **7** dots in total

☐ − ☐ = ☐

☐ − ☐ = ☐

b. **10** dots in total

☐ − ☐ = ☐

☐ − ☐ = ☐

c. **6** dots in total

☐ − ☐ = ☐

☐ − ☐ = ☐

d. **9** dots in total

☐ − ☐ = ☐

☐ − ☐ = ☐

e. **12** dots in total

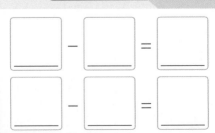

☐ − ☐ = ☐

☐ − ☐ = ☐

f. **11** dots in total

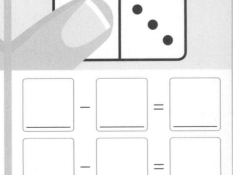

☐ − ☐ = ☐

☐ − ☐ = ☐

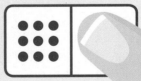
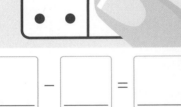

2. Write a subtraction fact to match each problem. Use **?** to show the unknown amount. You do not need to solve the problem.

a. There were 8 DVDs. I took some and there were 5 left. How many DVDs did I take?

☐ – ☐ = ☐

b. A cup has 4 ice cubes in it. 2 of the ice cubes melt completely. How many are left?

☐ – ☐ = ☐

c. 12 shells are on the beach. 9 are whole and the rest are broken. How many are broken?

☐ – ☐ = ☐

d. There are 2 more apples than oranges. There are 7 apples. How many oranges are there?

☐ – ☐ = ☐

3. Solve each problem. Show your thinking.

a. Ruth bought some seedlings. She planted 2 of them then there were 5 left. How many seedlings did she buy?

☐ seedlings

b. 12 berries are on a plate. Maka takes 10 of them then puts 3 back. How many berries are left on the plate?

☐ berries

Step Ahead   Solve the problem. Show your thinking on page 156.

Selena gets an allowance of $2 every week. Ruben gets $1 one week and $3 the next week. He gets an allowance in the same way every two weeks.

☐

Who will have more money after 7 weeks? _____

Think and Solve

You can only move ⟶ or ↑.

•⟶• is 1 unit.

How many units are in the shortest path from **A** to **B**? ☐

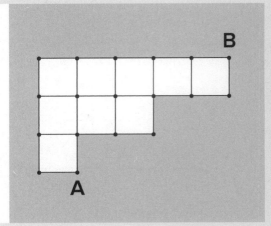

Words at Work

Write a subtraction word problem that you would solve by using the think-addition strategy.

_____

_____

_____

_____

_____

_____

_____

Write the addition and subtraction equations to match your problem.

_____

Ongoing Practice

1. Write the number on the expander in expanded form.

a.

☐ + ☐ + ☐

b.

☐ + ☐ + ☐

FROM 2.3.4

2. Figure out how many dots are covered. Then write the facts to match.

FROM 2.4.3

a. 12 dots in total

☐ + ☐ = ☐

☐ − ☐ = ☐

b. 8 dots in total

☐ + ☐ = ☐

☐ − ☐ = ☐

c. 11 dots in total

☐ + ☐ = ☐

☐ − ☐ = ☐

Preparing for Module 5

a. Write all the two-digit numbers you say when you start at 0 and count by 10s.

b. Write all the two-digit numbers you say when you start at 5 and count by 5s.

© ORIGO Education

ORIGO Stepping Stones · Grade 2 · 4.4

Step In

Rita wrote two stories to match this picture.

Addition story	Subtraction story
Five birds are on the fence and two are in the air. There are seven in total.	Seven birds were on the fence. Two flew away so five are left.

In each story the total is 7 and the parts are 5 and 2.

What addition and subtraction facts can you write with all three numbers?

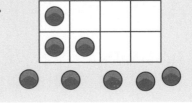

Four facts with the same parts and total together make a **fact family**.

Step Up

1. Write two addition facts to match each picture.
   Then write two subtraction facts to match.

a.

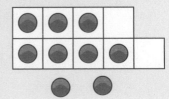

☐ + ☐ = 9

☐ + ☐ = 9

9 - ☐ = ☐

9 - ☐ = ☐

b.

☐ + ☐ = ☐

☐ + ☐ = ☐

☐ - ☐ = ☐

☐ - ☐ = ☐

c.

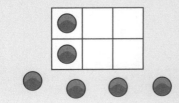

☐ + ☐ = ☐

☐ + ☐ = ☐

☐ - ☐ = ☐

☐ - ☐ = ☐

2. For each number fact, color the **total** red.
   Then color the **two parts** blue.

   a. $2 + 3 = 5$ b. $8 = 7 + 1$ c. $10 - 1 = 9$

   d. $7 - 3 = 4$ e. $6 = 0 + 6$ f. $7 + 3 = 10$

3. Cross out one fact that **does not** belong to each fact family.

   a.
   $2 + 1 = 3$
   $3 - 1 = 2$
   $1 + 2 = 3$
   $3 + 2 = 5$
   $3 - 2 = 1$

   b.
   $11 - 3 = 8$
   $11 - 8 = 3$
   $8 + 11 = 19$
   $3 + 8 = 11$
   $8 + 3 = 11$

   c.
   $6 - 2 = 4$
   $4 + 6 = 10$
   $4 + 2 = 6$
   $2 + 4 = 6$
   $6 - 4 = 2$

   d.
   $9 + 3 = 12$
   $9 - 3 = 6$
   $9 - 6 = 3$
   $3 + 6 = 9$
   $6 + 3 = 9$

4. Use the same color to show the number facts that belong
   in the same fact family.

   | $7 - 6 = 1$ | $2 + 6 = 8$ | $6 + 1 = 7$ | $8 - 6 = 2$ | $8 - 1 = 7$ |
   | $7 + 1 = 8$ | $7 - 1 = 6$ | $10 - 2 = 8$ | $1 + 7 = 8$ | $8 - 2 = 6$ |

Step Ahead   Write the related equations to complete these.

   a. $11 + 2 = 13$

   ___ + ___ = ___

   ___ − ___ = ___

   ___ − ___ = ___

   b. $3 + 15 = 18$

   ___ + ___ = ___

   ___ − ___ = ___

   ___ − ___ = ___

   c. $14 + 1 = 15$

   ___ + ___ = ___

   ___ − ___ = ___

   ___ − ___ = ___

Step In

Vishaya used cubes to measure the length of this pencil. She said it was 5 cubes long.

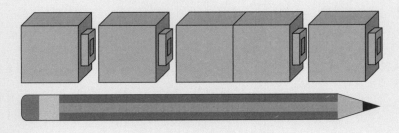

Is her measurement accurate? How do you know?

How would you use the cubes to measure the pencil?

I would join the cubes together so that there were no gaps and no overlaps.

Is the pencil longer or shorter than 5 cubes? How do you know?

Step Up

1. Make a cube train with 5 cubes. Color the pencils that are between 4 and 6 cubes long.

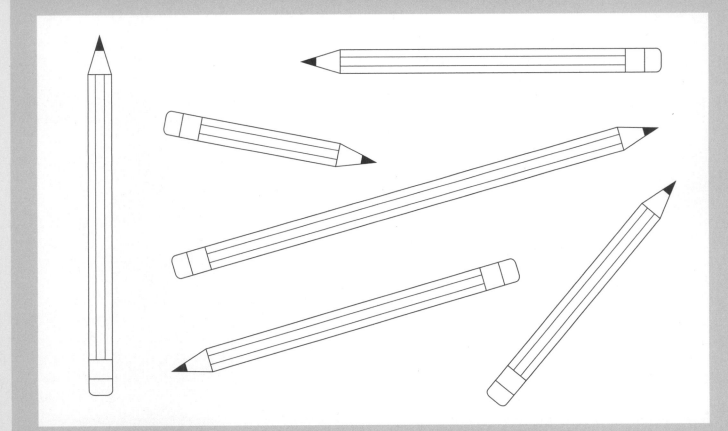

2. Measure the length of each pencil using cubes. Write the number.

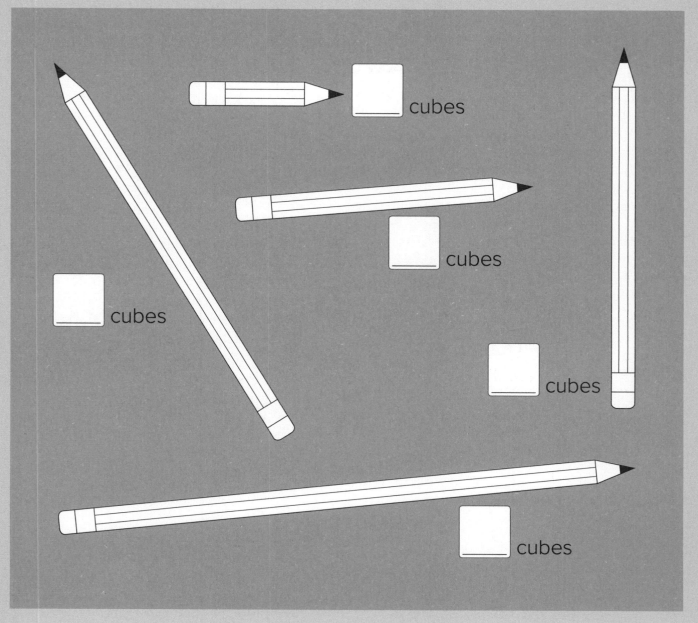

Step Ahead   Use cubes to help you draw a pencil that is **between** 5 and 7 cubes in length.

Computation Practice

What is one of the most common card games in the world?

★ Write all the totals.

★ Then write each letter above its matching total below.

3 + 5 = ☐   o   7 + 6 = ☐   e

5 + 9 = ☐   a   5 + 2 = ☐   r

3 + 7 = ☐   c   7 + 9 = ☐   l

8 + 4 = ☐   t   9 + 8 = ☐   n

9 + 6 = ☐   i   6 + 3 = ☐   s

3 + 8 = ☐   p

Some letters are used more than once.

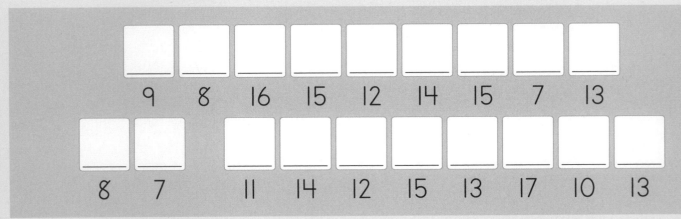

☐	☐	☐	☐	☐	☐	☐	☐	☐
9	8	16	15	12	14	15	7	13

☐	☐		☐	☐	☐	☐	☐	☐	☐	☐
8	7		11	14	12	15	13	17	10	13

1. Write **<**, **=**, or **>** to complete true sentences.

a.
303 ◯ 330

b.
521 ◯ 512

c.
630 ◯ 630

FROM 2.3.6

2. Write two addition facts to match each picture.
   Then write two subtraction facts to match.

FROM 2.4.5

a.
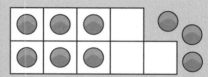

_____ + _____ = 9

_____ + _____ = 9

9 − _____ = _____

9 − _____ = _____

b.
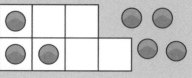

_____ + _____ = _____

_____ + _____ = _____

_____ − _____ = _____

_____ − _____ = _____

c.
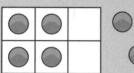

_____ + _____ = _____

_____ + _____ = _____

_____ − _____ = _____

_____ − _____ = _____

Preparing for Module 5

Write the make-ten equation that you would use
to figure out each total.

a.
see → $9 + 4$

think → ☐ + ☐ = ☐

b.
see → $8 + 6$

think → ☐ + ☐ = ☐

c.
see → $7 + 5$

think → ☐ + ☐ = ☐

d.
see → $9 + 7$

think → ☐ + ☐ = ☐

Step In | **What do you know about one inch?**

My dad said his shoe is about 10 inches long.

The store sells 6-inch subs.

What are some things that you think are about one inch long, one inch wide, or one inch thick?

Some books are about one inch thick.

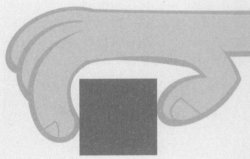

This pattern block is one inch long and one inch wide.

Use a pattern block to find some things in the classroom that measure one inch.

Step Up | I. Use your inch ruler to measure the length of each picture.

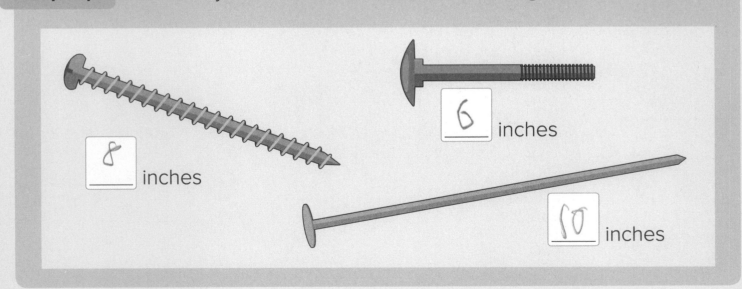

8 inches

6 inches

10 inches

2. Estimate the length of each picture first.
Then use your inch ruler to measure the length of each picture.

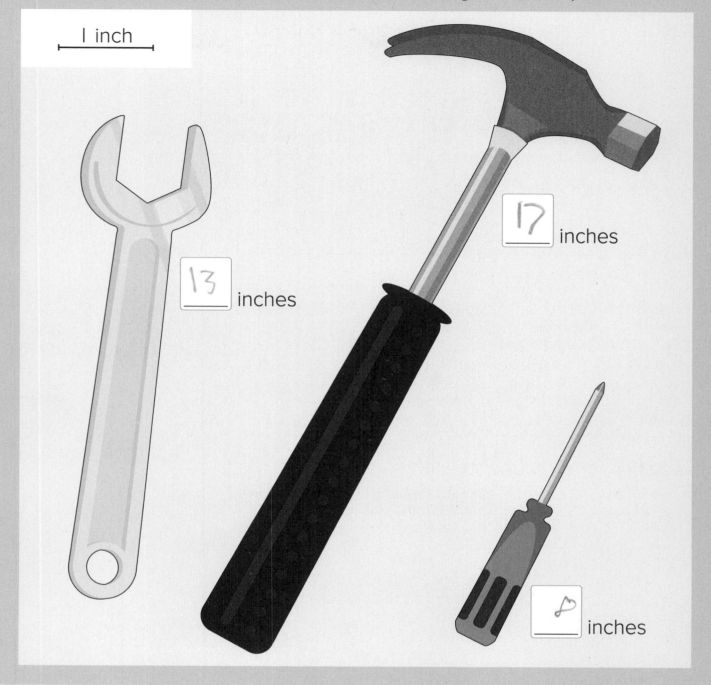

|← 1 inch →|

13 inches

17 inches

Ϙ inches

Step Ahead

Nails come in many shapes and sizes.
Draw a nail that is **between** 3 and 4 inches long.

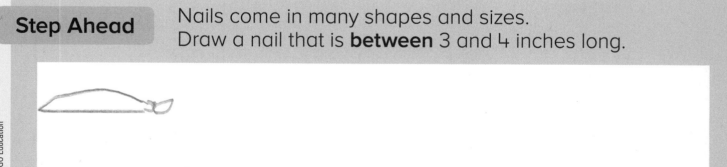

Step In   Which pencil is longer? How do you know?

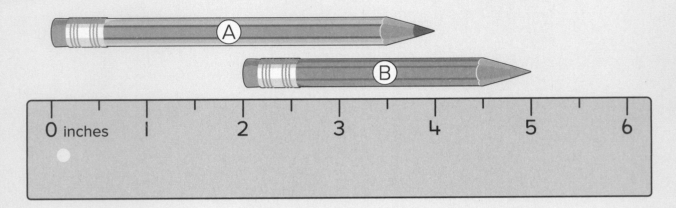

How did you figure out the length of each pencil?

How much longer is one pencil than the other?

> A short way to write inches is **in**.

Step Up   1.   Write the length of each pencil.

Pencil C	Pencil D	Pencil E	Pencil F
___ in	___ in	___ in	___ in

2. Write **longer** or **shorter** to complete each sentence. Use the information in Question 1 to help you.

a. Pencil F is _____ than Pencil E.

b. Pencil D is _____ than Pencil F.

c. Pencil C is _____ than Pencil F.

d. Pencil E is _____ than Pencil C.

e. Pencil E is _____ than Pencil C and Pencil D together.

3. Look at the pencils below.

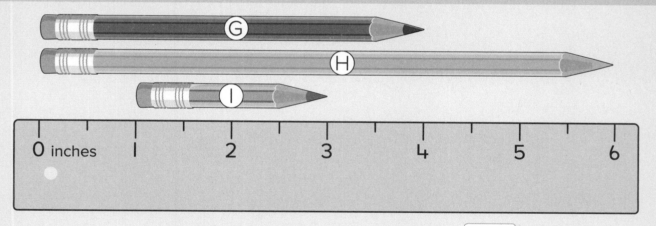

a. What is the difference in length between Pencil G and Pencil H? _____ in

b. What is the difference in length between Pencil H and Pencil I? _____ in

Step Ahead Look at the four pencils in Question 1. Write the letters shown on the pencils in order from **shortest** to **longest**.

_____ _____ _____ _____

Think and Solve Same shapes weigh the same.
Write the missing value inside each shape.

Circle the shape that is the lightest.

Words at Work Write in words how you solve this problem.

Felipe catches 18 fish. He throws 15 fish back. How many fish did he keep?

Ongoing Practice

1. Solve these problems. Think about the numbers on a hundred chart to help.

a. I am between 200 and 240. The digit in my hundreds place is the same as the digit in my tens place. You say me when you start at 200 and count by 10s.

b. I am between 270 and 300. The digit in my ones place is the same as the digit in my tens place. I have 9 ones.

2. Use your inch ruler to measure the length of each pencil. Color the pencil that is 4 inches long.

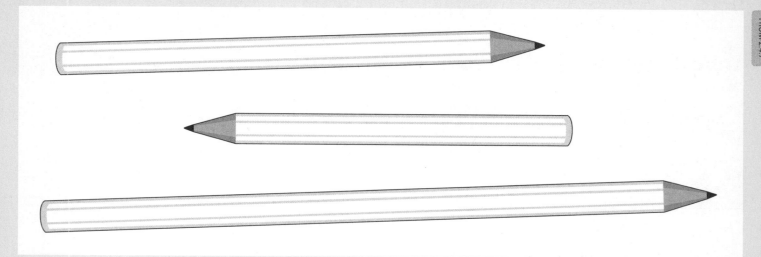

Preparing for Module 5

Add the two groups. Write the matching equation. You can use blocks to help.

a. 15   27

b. 38   39

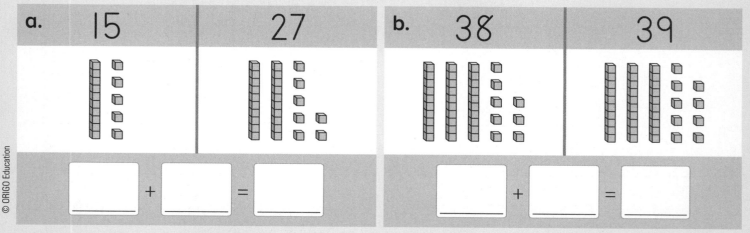

☐ + ☐ = ☐

☐ + ☐ = ☐

Step In What do you know about the unit of measure called a foot?

How long do you think it is?

The **foot** was once used to describe the length of a man's foot.

Imagine you measured the length of the classroom using your feet.

Would you get the same answer as your teacher? Explain your thinking.

These days, the foot is a standard length. Rulers are often one foot long. Use orange pattern blocks to measure the length of your ruler.

What do you notice?

What could you write to describe one foot?

One foot is the same length as 12 inches.

What are some things at home that measure about one foot long, one foot wide, or one foot thick?

A wooden spoon is about 1 foot long.

A big book could be 1 foot wide.

Some mattresses are about 1 foot thick.

Step Up 1. Look around the classroom.
Then write some objects that you would measure in feet.

2. Choose three objects in the room that you think are greater than one foot long or high.

a. Write the name of each object and estimate their length or height.

Object	My estimate
A	about _____ feet
B	about _____ feet
C	about _____ feet

b. Your teacher will help you make a tape measure. Use the tape measure to measure your objects. Then write their actual lengths or heights below.

Object A is about _____ feet.

Object B is about _____ feet.

Object C is about _____ feet.

Step Ahead

Complete the table. Then write how you found the missing numbers.

Feet	Inches
1	12
2	24
3	36
4	
5	

_____

_____

_____

_____

Step In How many inches equal one foot?

How many inches equal two feet?
How do you know?

How many inches taller than one foot is this plant?

How many more inches would the plant need to grow so it was two feet tall?

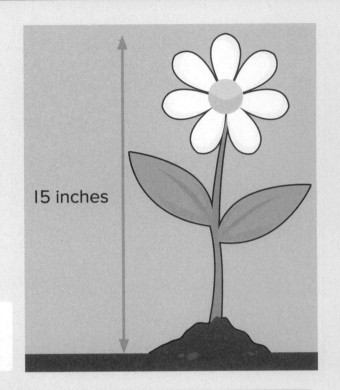

15 inches

I could say that the plant is I foot and 3 inches high.

Step Up I. This table shows the height of four plants.

Plant	Height
Daffodil	17 inches
Violet	8 inches
Daisy	15 inches
Marigold	19 inches

Complete these sentences.
Use the scale on the right to help.

a. The daffodil is ____ foot and ____ inches high.

b. The daisy is ____ foot and ____ inches high.

c. The marigold is ____ foot and ____ inches high.

d. The violet is ____ inches shorter than one foot high.

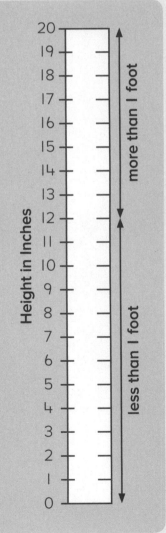

© ORIGO Education

2. Solve each problem. Show your thinking.

a. A baby carrot is 3 inches long.
A cucumber is 9 inches long.
How much shorter is the carrot
than the cucumber?

_____ in

b. The green hose is 6 feet
shorter than the purple hose.
The green hose is 9 feet long.
How long is the purple hose?

_____ ft

c. Morgan's plant is 2 inches
shorter than Jamar's plant.
Jamar's plant is 11 inches tall.
How tall is Morgan's plant?

_____ in

d. Two poles are placed on the
ground end-to-end. Their
total length is 13 feet. How
long might each pole be?

1st _____ ft   2nd _____ ft

e. A farmer measured the height of a corn plant as 9 inches.
He measured it again one week later and the plant is now
5 inches taller. How much taller than one foot is it now?

_____ in

Step Ahead   Write these lengths in order from **shortest** to **longest**.

| 17 in | 1 ft 6 in | 14 in | 1 ft 3 in |

| _____ | _____ | _____ | _____ |

Computation Practice

★ Write all the totals.
★ Draw a line to the astronaut that matches each total.

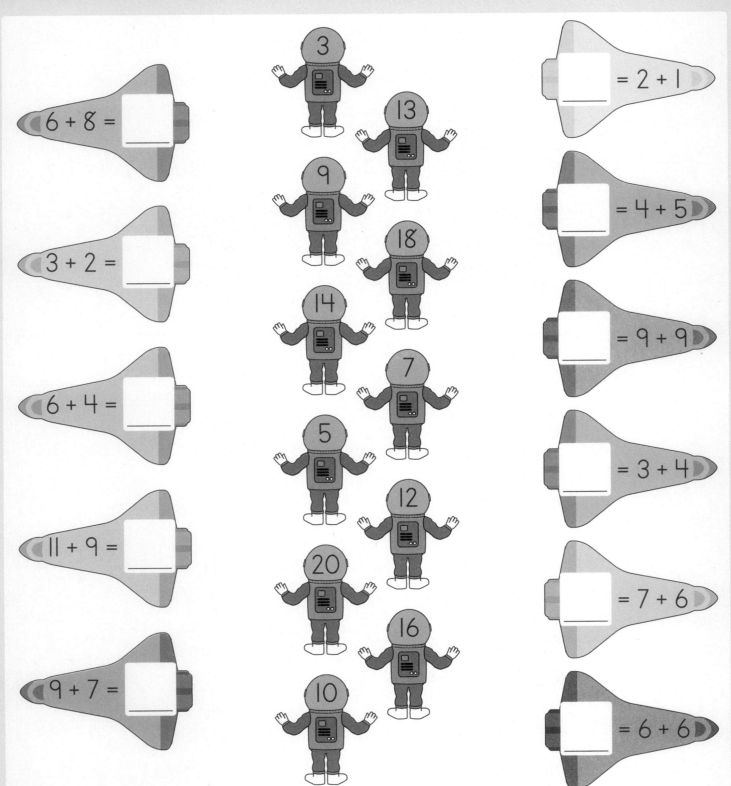

6 + 8 = ___

3 + 2 = ___

6 + 4 = ___

11 + 9 = ___

9 + 7 = ___

___ = 2 + 1

___ = 4 + 5

___ = 9 + 9

___ = 3 + 4

___ = 7 + 6

___ = 6 + 6

3 13 9 18 14 7 5 12 20 16 10

1. Color one part of each strip red. Then circle the strip that shows **one-half** red.

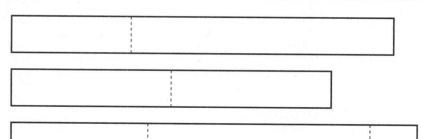

FROM 1.6.8

2. Write the names of some objects at home that you would measure in feet.

FROM 2.4.9

Preparing for Module 5

Figure out the number of dots that are covered. Then complete the facts.

a.

9 – 4 = _____

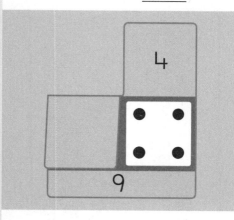

4

9

4 + _____ = 9

b.

12 – 5 = _____

5

12

5 + _____ = 12

c.

16 – 9 = _____

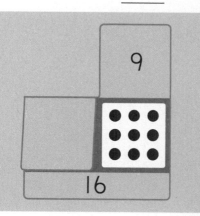

9

16

9 + _____ = 16

Step In   How could you measure things like a sports track or a building?

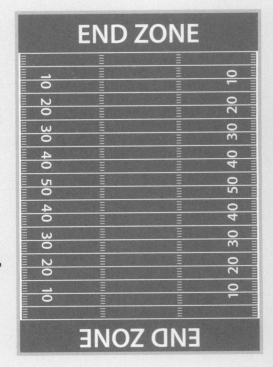

Look at the classroom yardstick.
What do you notice?

How long is one yard?

How many feet equal one yard?
How can you figure out the number of inches that equal one yard?

What are some things that are about one yard long, one yard wide, or one yard thick?

A baseball bat is nearly 1 yard long.

A door is about 1 yard wide.

A big tree could be 1 yard thick.

Step Up   1. Your teacher will show you some lengths of string. Write your estimate for each string. Your teacher will then help you measure the actual length.

String	My estimate	Actual length
A	yards	yards
B	yards	yards
C	yards	yards
D	yards	yards

2. Write one object that you think could match each length.

a. 2 yards

b. 5 yards

c. 10 yards

d. 50 yards

3. Measure each length.

a. The classroom is about _____ yards **long**.

b. The classroom is about _____ yards **wide**.

c. The library is about _____ yards **long**.

d. The library is about _____ yards **wide**.

Step Ahead

Complete the table. Then write how you found the missing numbers.

Yards	Feet
1	3
2	6
3	9
4	
5	
10	

Step In

Think about the measurement units of inches, feet, and yards.

What types of things do you think it would be **most** useful to measure in inches?

What types of things do you think it would be **least** useful to measure in inches?

Which unit would be better to use? Why?

A short way to write feet is ft.
A short way to write yards is yd.

Step Up

1. Write **inches**, **feet**, or **yards** to show how you would measure each of these.

a. pen _____

b. running track _____

c. whiteboard _____

d. cell phone _____

e. building _____

f. adult's height _____

2. Identify four objects in your classroom that you think are between 1 and 2 yards long. Write them below.

a. Object A _____

b. Object B _____

c. Object C _____

d. Object D _____

3. Measure the length of your objects in inches.

A is ____ in   B is ____ in   C is ____ in   D is ____ in

4. Measure the length of your objects in feet.

A is ____ ft   B is ____ ft   C is ____ ft   D is ____ ft

5. Look at your answers for Questions 3 and 4. Why does each object have a fewer number of feet than inches?

_____

_____

_____

_____

Step Ahead   Solve this problem. Show your thinking.

Sammy Snail and Bindi Beetle are 12 inches apart and looking at each other. If Sammy moves forward one inch, Bindi will move forward 2 inches. How many inches does Sammy have to move forward so that he and Bindi are nose to nose?

____ in

Think and Solve

This map shows a bus route. Trace over the lines in red to show the **shortest** trip between Redcliffe and Monto. Write the total time.

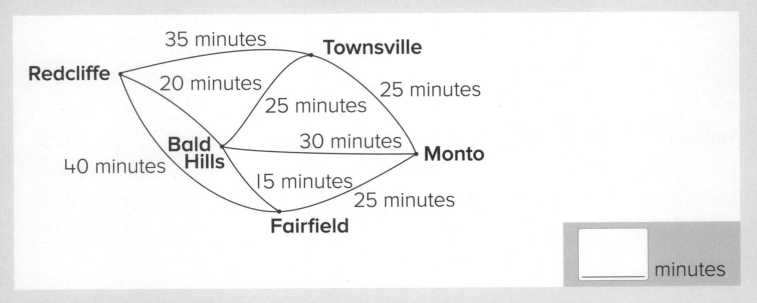

_____ minutes

Words at Work

Write the answer for each clue in the grid. Use words from the list. One word is not used.

Clues Across

1. One foot is the same length as ___ inches.

4. You can ___ addition to figure out a subtraction problem.

5. Related facts have the same ___ and two parts.

6. The ___ is a small unit of length.

Clues Down

2. You can use a ruler to measure ___.

3. There are four facts in a fact ___.

inch	think
length	total
twelve	family
foot	

© ORIGO Education

Ongoing Practice

I. Color one part of each shape red. Then circle the fraction name that describes the red part.

a.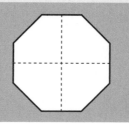

one-half   one-fourth

b.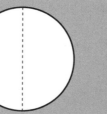

one-half   one-fourth

c.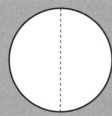

one-half   one-fourth

2. Write **inches**, **feet**, or **yards** to show how you would measure the length of each of these.

a. paper clip _____

b. swimming pool _____

c. your arm _____

d. car _____

e. bicycle _____

f. tens block _____

Preparing for Module 5   Write the fact family to match each picture.

a

___ + ___ = ___

___ + ___ = ___

___ − ___ = ___

___ − ___ = ___

b.

___ + ___ = ___

___ + ___ = ___

___ − ___ = ___

___ − ___ = ___

c.

___ + ___ = ___

___ + ___ = ___

___ − ___ = ___

___ − ___ = ___

Step In

What is the total cost of these clothes?

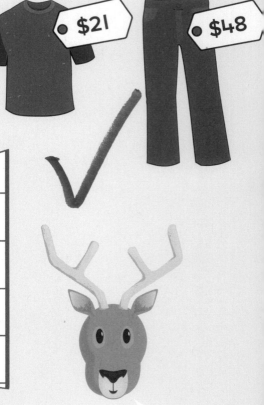

$21

$48

How did you figure it out?

How could you use a hundred chart
to show how you add the two numbers?

21	22	23	24	25	26	27	28	29	30
31	32	33	34	35	36	37	38	39	40
41	42	43	44	45	46	47	48	49	50
51	52	53	54	55	56	57	58	59	60
61	62	63	64	65	66	67	68	69	70

I would start with 48 and
work with the ones first.
48 plus 1 is 49. 49 plus 20 is 69.

I would start with 48 and
add the tens first. 48 plus
20 is 68. Then 1 more is 69.

Which method do you like best? Why?

Why does each method start with the number that is greater?

Step Up

1. Draw arrows on the chart above to show how you add
each of these. Then write the totals.

a. 54 + 11 = 70 65

b. 43 + 23 = 66

c. 49 + 11 = 60

d. 28 + 12 = 40

e. 35 + 21 = 69 56

f. 41 + 21 = 62

g. 22 + 11 = 33

h. 37 + 31 = 68

i. 21 + 13 = 33 34

2. Start with the greater number. Write equations to show how
you add **the tens**, **then the ones**. Then write the total.

a.

62 + 34 = (910) de

| 62 | + | 30 | = | 92 |
| 92 | + | 4 | = | 96 |

b.

74 + 15 = 89

| 74 | + | 10 | = | 84 |
| 84 | + | 5 | = | 89 |

c.

16 + 83 = (10 99)

| 8 | + | 7 | = | 20 |
| 19 | + | 4 | = | 10 |

d.

46 + 32 = (8)

| 1 | + | 4 | = | 8 |
| 6 | + | 20 | = | 1 |

3. Start with the greater number. Write equations to show how
you add **the ones**, **then the tens**. Then write the total.

a.

56 + 21 = (47) n

| 56 | + | 1 | = | 57 |
| 57 | + | 20 | = | 40 |

b.

66 + 13 = (5) a

| 10 | + | 13 | = | 19 |
| 14 | + | 16 | = | 20 |

Step Ahead   Write the missing numbers along this trail.

15 →+13→ 28 →+21→ 42 →+11→ (63) 60 →+22→ (72) 82

Step In **Andrea rolls the cube.**

She finds the number that she rolled on the number line.
Then she makes jumps of 10 from that number.

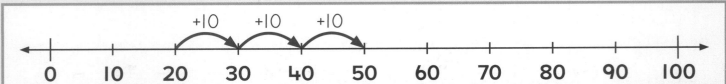

Do you think that Andrea will land on the number 90?
How do you know? What other numbers will Andrea land on?

Connor rolls 5. He then makes jumps of 10 from that number.

Do you think that he will land on the number 50?
What numbers will Connor land on?

What happens if you roll 17? What numbers will you
say if you make jumps of ten from that number?

Step Up 1. Draw jumps of 10 to reach the end of the number line.
Write the numbers that you land on.

a.

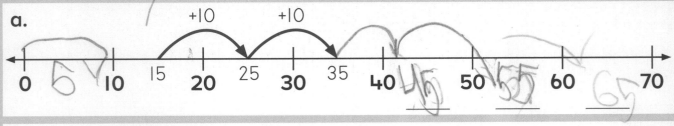

b.

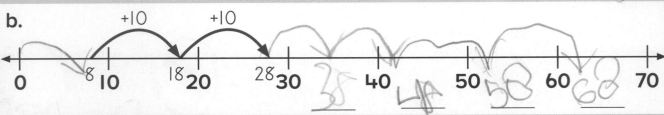

2. Show the position of the number on the number line. Then write the numbers that you will land on if you make jumps of 10.

a.

16

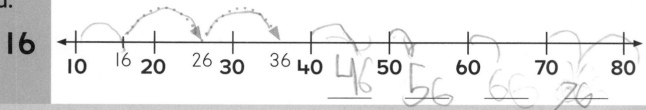

10   ¹⁶ 20   ²⁶ 30   ³⁶ 40   50   60   70   80

_46_ _56_ _66_ _76_

b.

32

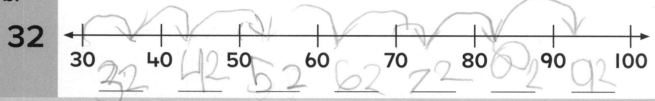

30   40   50   60   70   80   90   100

_32_ _42_ _52_ _62_ _72_ _82_ _92_

3. Show the position of the number on the number line. Then write the numbers that you will land on if you make jumps of 5.

a.

6

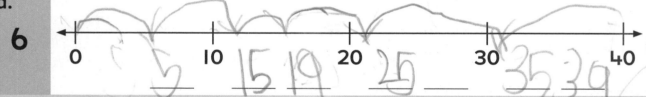

0   10   20   30   40

_6_ _15_ _19_ _25_ _35_ _39_

b.

52

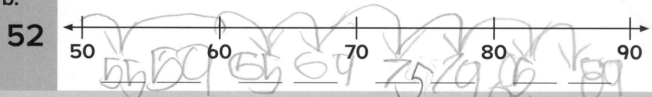

50   60   70   80   90

_57_ _60_ _69_ _64_ _75_ _79_ _86_ _89_

Step Ahead   Use skip counting to figure out the total amount shown.

_____ ¢

Computation Practice   What did the pig say to the farmer?

★ Write all the differences.
★ Then write each letter above its matching difference at the bottom of the page.

75 – 2 = ☐   g   58 – 20 = ☐   l

63 – 10 = ☐   o   89 – 10 = ☐   h

91 – 20 = ☐   a   72 – 2 = ☐   i

84 – 1 = ☐   c   25 – 1 = ☐   s

47 – 10 = ☐   t   68 – 20 = ☐   k

21 – 1 = ☐   p   49 – 2 = ☐   n

Some letters are used more than once.

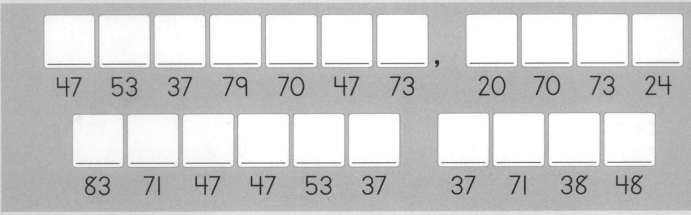

☐ ☐ ☐ ☐ ☐ ☐ ☐ , ☐ ☐ ☐ ☐
47 53 37 79 70 47 73   20 70 73 24

☐ ☐ ☐ ☐ ☐ ☐   ☐ ☐ ☐ ☐
83 71 47 47 53 37   37 71 38 48

ORIGO Stepping Stones · Grade 2 · 5.2

Ongoing Practice

1. Write an equation to match what is shown on each number track.

a.

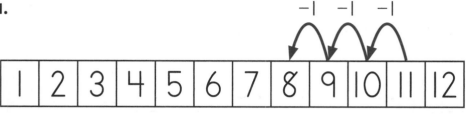

☐ − ☐ = ☐

b.

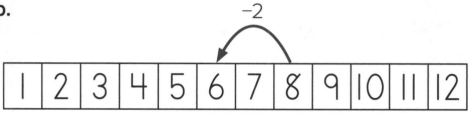

☐ − ☐ = ☐

2. Start with the greater number. Write addition equations to show how you **add the tens, then the ones**. Then write the total.

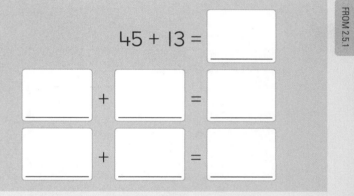

a.

73 + 24 = ☐

☐ + ☐ = ☐

☐ + ☐ = ☐

b.

45 + 13 = ☐

☐ + ☐ = ☐

☐ + ☐ = ☐

Preparing for Module 6

Add the two groups.
Then write the matching equation.

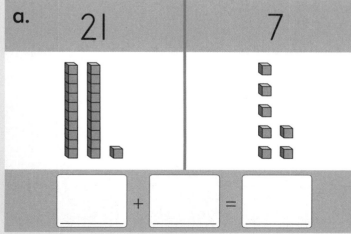

a. 21   7

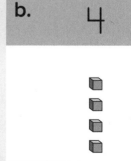

☐ + ☐ = ☐

b. 4   33

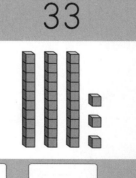

☐ + ☐ = ☐

Step In

How can you figure out the total cost of the guitar and book?

How could you use this number line to show how you added?

$73

CHORDS FOR BEGINNERS

$14

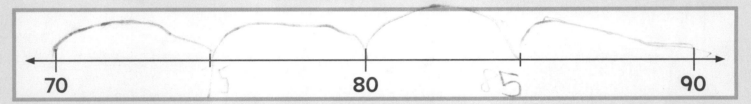

70   80   85   90

I started at 73 and added the tens, then the ones of 14. I can draw jumps like this to show how I added.

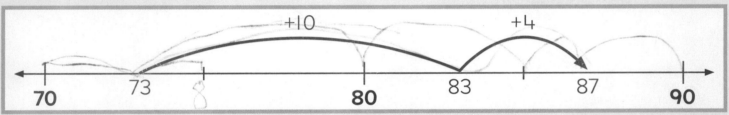

+10   +4

70   73   80   83   87   90

Step Up

1. a. Draw jumps on this number line to show how you would add 56 and 13.

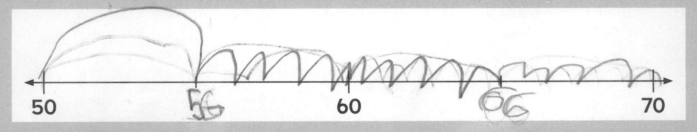

50   56   60   66   70

b. Draw jumps on this number line to show **another way** you could add 56 and 13.

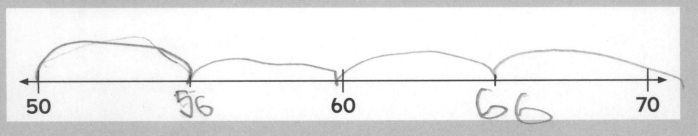

50   56   60   66   70

2. Draw jumps to show how you could count on to figure out each of these. Then write the totals.

a. ✓

$46 + 12 = \boxed{58}$

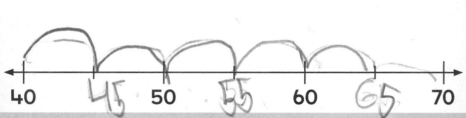

40   45   50   55   60   65   70

b.

$35 + 21 = \boxed{56}$

30   35   40   45   50   55   60

c.

$62 + 27 = \boxed{89}$

60   65   70   75   80   85   90

d.

$55 + 24 = \boxed{79}$

50   55   60   65   70   75   80

e.

$33 + 16 = \boxed{49}$

30   35   40   45   50   55   60

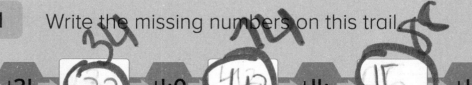

13 → +21 → 34 (22) → +40 → 74 (42) → +14 → 86 (15) → +11 → 99 (12)

Step In

How would you use the ten-frames to figure out 18 + 5?

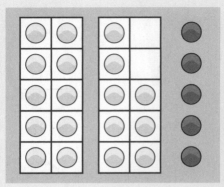

I would fill the second ten-frame to make another ten. It's much easier to figure out 20 + 3 than 18 + 5.

Monique uses the number line to show how she figured out 18 + 5.

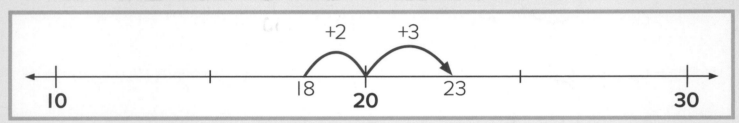

What thinking did she use? What is similar about each method?

How could you use the make-ten strategy to add 28 + 5?

What are some other numbers you could add using this strategy?

Step Up

1. Look at the number line. Complete the equation to match.

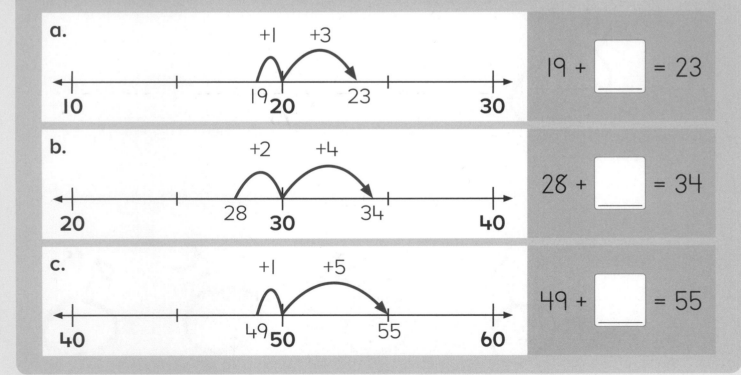

a.

$19 + \boxed{} = 23$

b.

$28 + \boxed{} = 34$

c.

$49 + \boxed{} = 55$

2. Figure out the total. Then draw jumps on the number line to show your thinking.

a.

$29 + 4 =$ ☐

```
  +----+--------+--------+--------+----+
  20           30                 40
```

b.

$6 + 58 =$ ☐

```
  +----+--------+--------+--------+----+
  50           60                 70
```

c.

$47 + 5 =$ ☐

```
  +----+--------+--------+--------+----+
  40           50                 60
```

d.

$7 + 38 =$ ☐

```
  +----+--------+--------+--------+----+
  30           40                 50
```

e.

$69 + 8 =$ ☐

```
  +----+--------+--------+--------+----+
  60           70                 80
```

Step Ahead

Dorothy has a quarter, two dimes, and three pennies. Jacob has a nickel and four pennies.

a. How much more money does Dorothy have than Jacob? ☐ ¢

b. How much money do they have in total? ☐ ¢

Think and Solve Look at these numbers.

a. Use different colors to show pairs of numbers that add to 20.

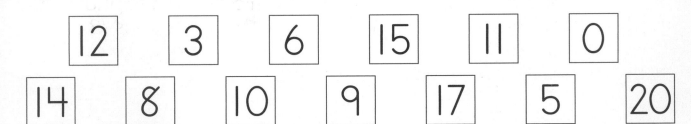

12   3   6   15   11   0

14   8   10   9   17   5   20

b. Circle the number that is left over. Then use that number to complete this equation.

[ ] + [ ] = 20

c. Use two numbers that are not shown above to complete this equation.

[ ] + [ ] = 20

Words at Work Imagine your friend is away from school when you are learning about using the make-ten strategy to add numbers like 28 and 7. Write how you would explain the strategy to them.

Ongoing Practice

1. Write a subtraction equation to match each problem. Use **?** to show the unknown amount. You do not need to solve the problems.

a. Max has 12 books about birds. He gave some books to Peta. There are 8 books left. How many books did he give Peta?

$$\underline{\hspace{2cm}} - \underline{\hspace{2cm}} = \underline{\hspace{2cm}}$$

b. Antonio has 5 cents more than Patricia. Antonio has 13 cents. How much money does Patricia have?

$$\underline{\hspace{2cm}} - \underline{\hspace{2cm}} = \underline{\hspace{2cm}}$$

FROM 2.4.4

2. Write the totals. Then draw jumps on the number line to show your thinking.

FROM 2.5.4

a.

$68 + 5 = \boxed{}$

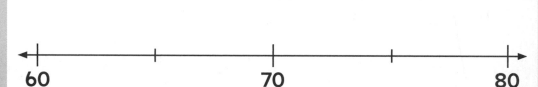

60   70   80

b.

$8 + 47 = \boxed{}$

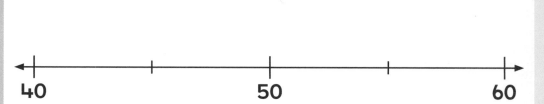

40   50   60

Preparing for Module 6

Write the number of ones blocks. Circle 10 ones. Then write the number of tens and ones.

a.

$\boxed{}$ ones

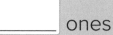

$\boxed{}$ ten $\boxed{}$ ones

b.

$\boxed{}$ ones

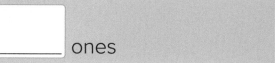

$\boxed{}$ ten $\boxed{}$ ones

Step In

Do you think that the total cost of these two items is more or less than $40?

 $16

 $28

How did you decide?

Amber uses a number line to figure out the total cost.

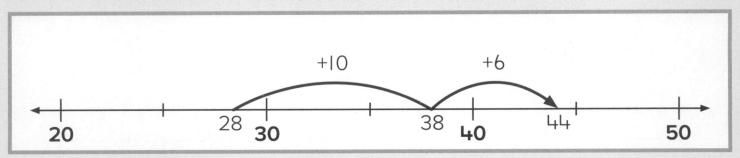

What steps does Amber follow?

Jerome uses a different method.

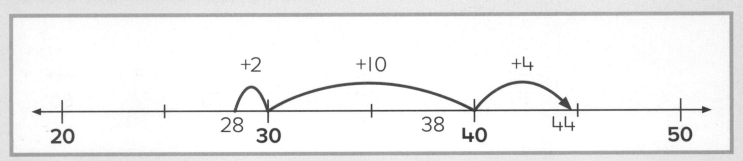

What steps does Jerome follow?

Which method do you prefer? Why?

Step Up

1. Figure out the total.
   Draw jumps on the number line to show your thinking.

   27 + 17 = _____

   20   30   40   50

2. Figure out each total.
Draw jumps on the number line to show your thinking.

a.

38 + 15 = _____

```
+----+----+----+----+----+----+
30        40        50        60
```

b.

57 + 26 = _____

```
+----+----+----+----+----+----+----+----+
50        60        70        80        90
```

c.

28 + 46 = _____

```
+----+----+----+----+----+----+----+----+
40        50        60        70        80
```

Step Ahead   Yasmin uses this method to record 47 + 16. Write the total.

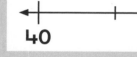

47 + 16 = ☐

47 → +10 → 57 → +6 → 63

Use the same method to record 68 + 24. Then write the total.

68 + 24 = ☐

68 → ☐ → ⋆ → ☐ → ⋆

Step In   Amy has $100 in savings.

Does she have enough money to buy both
of these items? How did you decide?

Amy figures out the total cost on a number line.

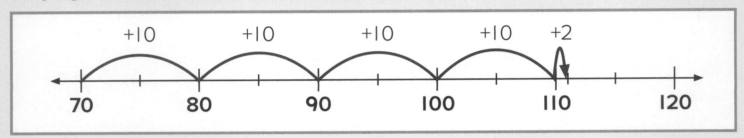

What steps does Amy follow?

How could you figure out the
total cost with fewer jumps?

I would start at 70 and
make one jump to 100.
I would then add the
amount that is left over.

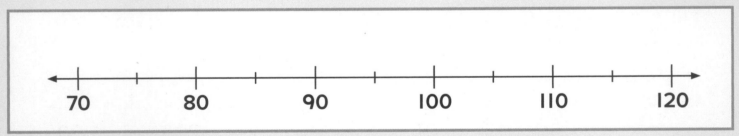

How could you use the number line to figure out 75 + 34?

Step Up   1. Figure out the total. Draw jumps on the number line
to show your thinking.

80 + 30 = _____

© ORIGO Education

2. Figure out the total. Show your thinking.

a. 75 + 40 = _____

b. 30 + 87 = _____

c. 85 + 22 = _____

d. 27 + 92 = _____

Step Ahead Write an equation that you think matches this number line.

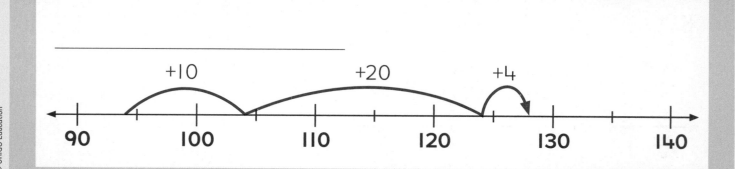

5.6 Maintaining concepts and skills

Computation Practice

★ Complete the facts as fast as you can.

start

10 - 6 = ____

12 - 9 = ____

7 - 2 = ____

9 - 3 = ____

18 - 8 = ____

13 - 7 = ____

14 - 6 = ____

16 - 7 = ____

11 - 5 = ____

8 - 3 = ____

17 - 8 = ____

6 - 4 = ____

5 - 2 = ____

4 - 3 = ____

12 - 3 = ____

15 - 6 = ____

9 - 4 = ____

10 - 3 = ____

14 - 9 = ____

13 - 5 = ____

finish

1. Look around the classroom. Then write some objects that you would measure in inches.

2. Figure out the total. Draw jumps to show your thinking.

a. 30 + 87 = _____

b. 89 + 36 = _____

Preparing for Module 6

Add the two groups.
Then write the matching equation.

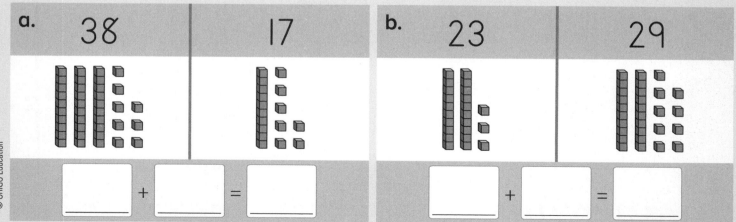

a. 38   17

☐ + ☐ = ☐

b. 23   29

☐ + ☐ = ☐

Step In

Do you think that these two items cost more or less than $100? How did you decide?

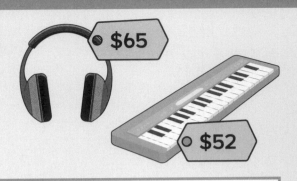

$65

$52

How could you figure out the total cost on this empty number line?

Sometimes it's easier to show your thinking on an empty number line because you don't have to think about the exact position of each number.

Yuma decides to make these jumps.

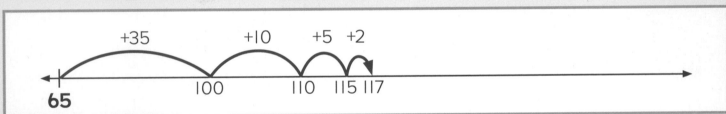

+35   +10   +5 +2

65   100   110 115 117

Why does he start the number line at 65 and not 0?

How does he add the cost of the keyboard? What jumps does he make?

What is another way to figure out the total cost?

Step Up

1. Figure out the total. Draw jumps and write numbers on the number line to show your thinking.

50 + 37 = _____

2. Figure out the total. Show your thinking.

a.

$36 + 60 =$ ☐

⟵―――――――――――――――――――――――――⟶

b.

$67 + 5 =$ ☐

⟵―――――――――――――――――――――――――⟶

c.

$80 + 34 =$ ☐

⟵―――――――――――――――――――――――――⟶

d.

$95 + 12 =$ ☐

⟵―――――――――――――――――――――――――⟶

e.

$72 + 51 =$ ☐

⟵―――――――――――――――――――――――――⟶

Step Ahead Write the missing numbers in each box. Then complete the equation.

a.

$80 + 38 =$ ☐

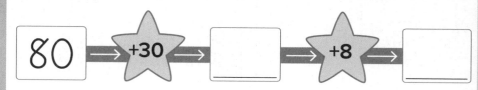

b.

$75 + 43 =$ ☐

Subtraction: Reviewing the think-addition strategy (doubles facts)

Step In

There are 15 cows on this farm. Some of the cows are in the barn.

How could you figure out the number of cows in the barn?

I could start with 15 and take away 7, or I could think **7 plus something is 15**.

Step Up

1. Write the two parts and the total for each picture.

a.

One part is _____.

The other part is _____.

The total is _____.

b.

One part is _____.

The other part is _____.

The total is _____.

2. Figure out how many dots are covered. Then write addition and subtraction facts to match.

a. **9** dots in total	b. **13** dots in total	c. **11** dots in total

___ + ___ = ___	___ + ___ = ___	___ + ___ = ___
___ − ___ = ___	___ − ___ = ___	___ − ___ = ___

d. **17** dots in total	e. **14** dots in total	f. **16** dots in total
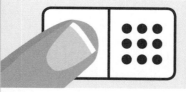		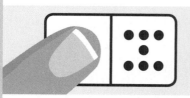
___ + ___ = ___	___ + ___ = ___	___ + ___ = ___
___ − ___ = ___	___ − ___ = ___	___ − ___ = ___

Step Ahead   Write the missing numbers along the trail.

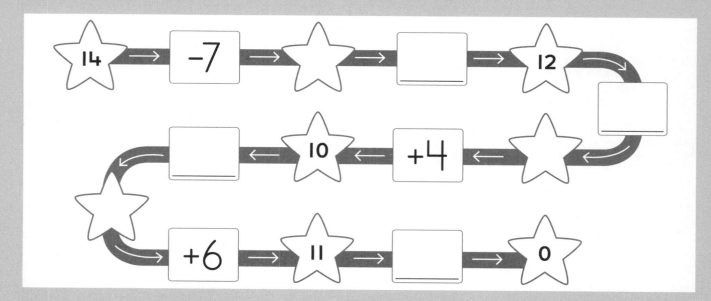

Think and Solve

 +  = $10    = $12

a. Figure out a possible price for each toy.

 $_____   🐴 $_____   ✈ $_____

b. Show another possible price for each toy.

 $_____   🐴 $_____   ✈ $_____

Words at Work

a. Write two different two-digit numbers that have more than 5 tens and fewer than 4 ones.

[ ] [ ]

b. Write an addition problem using the numbers.

c. Write how you figure out the total.

© ORIGO Education

1. a. Draw a pencil that is **exactly** 6 inches long.
   b. Draw a pencil that is **shorter than** 6 inches long.

FROM 2.4.8

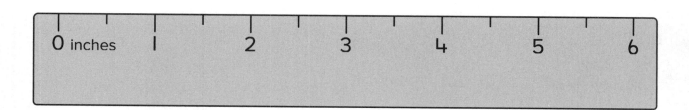

2. Figure out how many dots are covered. Then write the facts to match.

FROM 2.5.8

| a. | 8 dots in total | b. | 10 dots in total | c. | 15 dots in total |

☐ + ☐ = ☐
☐ − ☐ = ☐

☐ + ☐ = ☐
☐ − ☐ = ☐

☐ + ☐ = ☐
☐ − ☐ = ☐

Preparing for Module 6   For each number, write the **ten** that is closest.

70   80   90

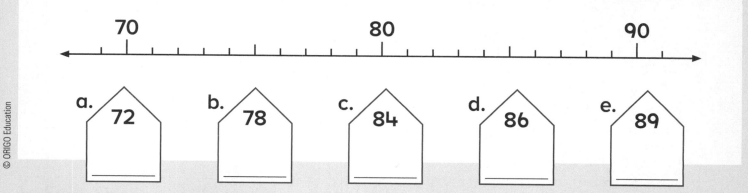

a. 72   b. 78   c. 84   d. 86   e. 89

Step In

There were some plates in the cabinet. Matthew took out 5 large plates with a blue edge. Now there are 7 plates in the cabinet. How many plates were in the cabinet before?

What information helps you solve the problem?

What addition equation can you write to match the story?

What subtraction equation can you write?

I could write 7 + 5 = ? to show it as addition.
I could write ? - 5 = 7 to show it as subtraction.
The unknown number is the same in both equations.

Step Up

1. Draw dots to help you complete the subtraction fact. Then complete the related addition fact.

a.

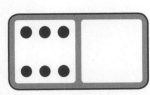

13 − 6 = ☐

6 + ☐ = 13

b.

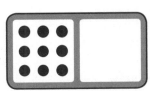

17 − 9 = ☐

9 + ☐ = 17

c.

11 − 5 = ☐

5 + ☐ = 11

d.

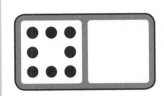

15 − 8 = ☐

8 + ☐ = 15

2. Draw dots to help you complete the equations.

a.

$$10 - 6 = \underline{}$$

$$\underline{} + \underline{} = \underline{}$$

b.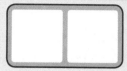

$$14 - 6 = \underline{}$$

$$\underline{} + \underline{} = \underline{}$$

3. Write a **subtraction** equation to match each word problem. Use **?** to show the unknown amount. You do not need to solve the problem.

a. Arleen bought 16 stickers. She used 9 of them. How many does she have left?

b. Beth has 7 books fewer than Joel. Joel has 15 books. How many books does Beth have?

c. Sandra put 6 muffins on a plate. The plate can hold 14 muffins. How many more muffins can Sandra fit on the plate?

d. Sharon and Steven have 12 berries together. Steven has 5 berries. How many berries does Sharon have?

Step Ahead

Complete each equation in the picture on the left. Then write different numbers to complete the equations on the right.

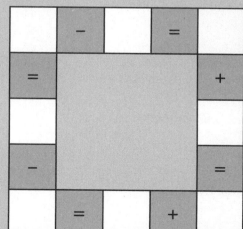

© ORIGO Education

Step In

There were 15 cans in a box. Norton put some cans on a shelf. There were 8 cans left in the box. How many cans did Norton put on the shelf?

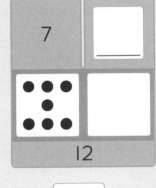

What addition fact can you use to help you figure out the answer?

What strategy could you use to solve that addition fact?

I can solve many subtraction facts by using more than one addition strategy.

Look at these subtraction facts.

$11 - 2 = ?$ $14 - 6 = ?$ $12 - 4 = ?$ $18 - 9 = ?$

Think about the addition facts you would use to solve them.

What strategies could you use to solve those addition facts?

Step Up

1. Write the missing number and draw the matching dots on each card. Then complete the addition facts.

a.

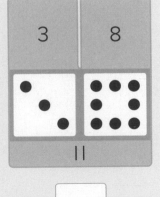

$3 + \boxed{} = 11$

b.

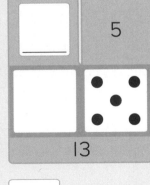

$\boxed{} + 5 = 13$

c.

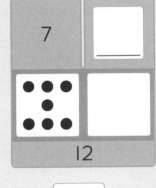

$7 + \boxed{} = 12$

2. Figure out how many dots are covered.
Then write the matching equations.

a. 13 dots in total

☐ + ☐ = ☐

☐ − ☐ = ☐

b. 16 dots in total

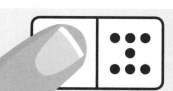

☐ + ☐ = ☐

☐ − ☐ = ☐

c. 11 dots in total

☐ + ☐ = ☐

☐ − ☐ = ☐

d. 15 dots in total

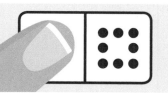

☐ + ☐ = ☐

☐ − ☐ = ☐

e. 17 dots in total

☐ + ☐ = ☐

☐ − ☐ = ☐

f. 12 dots in total

☐ + ☐ = ☐

☐ − ☐ = ☐

Step Ahead

Write the missing numbers to complete true equations
going down and across.

14			+		=	15
−		+		−		−
		4	4	+		=	13
=		=	=		=	
3	+		=		3	

Computation Practice

★ To discover an amazing fact, write all the totals.
★ Then write each letter above its matching total at the bottom of the page.

26 + 10 = _____ **n**   17 + 20 = _____ **h**

36 + 20 = _____ **s**   41 + 10 = _____ **r**

65 + 20 = _____ **p**   72 + 20 = _____ **c**

33 + 10 = _____ **a**   10 + 19 = _____ **o**

20 + 28 = _____ **u**   20 + 25 = _____ **t**

10 + 51 = _____ **e**

Some letters are used more than once.

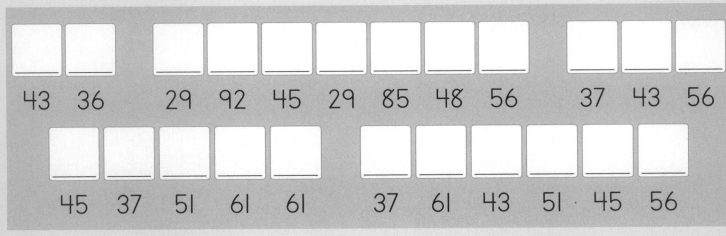

43	36	29	92	45	29	85	48	56	37	43	56

45	37	51	61	61	37	61	43	51	45	56

1. Solve each problem. Show your thinking.

a. Emilio's shoe is 2 inches shorter than his brother's shoe. His brother's shoe is 9 inches long. How long is Emilio's shoe?

FROM 2.4.10

_____ inches

b. Zoe cut a piece of pipe 12 feet long and a piece 7 feet long. What is the difference in length between the two pieces?

_____ feet

2. Figure out how many dots are covered and write equations to match.

FROM 2.5.10

| a. | 15 dots in total | b. | 12 dots in total | c. | 17 dots in total |

☐ + ☐ = ☐

☐ − ☐ = ☐

☐ + ☐ = ☐

☐ − ☐ = ☐

☐ + ☐ = ☐

☐ − ☐ = ☐

Preparing for Module 6

Each 😊 means one vote. Use the graph to answer the questions below.

Do You Like Eating Vegetables?								
Yes	😊	😊	😊	😊	😊	😊	😊	😊
No	😊	😊	😊					

a. How many children like eating vegetables? ☐

b. How many children do not like eating vegetables? ☐

c. How many children voted in total? ☐

Step In

A fish tank has 13 fish in it. Some fish hide in the plants and only 5 fish can be seen. Then another 2 fish hide in the plants. How many fish are hiding now?

What operations could you use to solve this problem?
Which addition or subtraction facts could you use?
What steps do you need to take?

Step Up

1. Draw dots to help you complete the subtraction fact. Then write a related addition fact.

a.

$12 - 3 = \boxed{}$

$3 + \boxed{} = 12$

b.
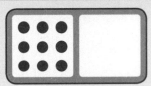

$15 - 9 = \boxed{}$

$9 + \boxed{} = 15$

c.

$11 - 8 = \boxed{}$

$8 + \boxed{} = 11$

d.

$13 - 9 = \boxed{}$

$9 + \boxed{} = 13$

e.

$12 - 8 = \boxed{}$

$\boxed{} + \boxed{} = \boxed{}$

f.

$14 - 5 = \boxed{}$

$\boxed{} + \boxed{} = \boxed{}$

2. Solve each problem. Show your thinking.

a. Olivia has 11 tadpoles in a jar. 4 of them have legs and the rest do not. How many tadpoles do not have legs?

☐ tadpoles

b. There are 7 beetles with stripes and 13 beetles with spots. How many fewer beetles have stripes than spots?

☐ beetles

c. A plant has 15 berries. 6 of the berries are green and the rest are red. Vincent ate 5 of the red berries. How many red berries are there now?

☐ berries

d. 12 squirrels were playing in the park. Some ran up a tree and 5 stayed on the ground. Then 2 more squirrels went up the tree. How many squirrels are in the tree now?

☐ squirrels

Step Ahead

The green vase has 8 more flowers than the yellow vase but 3 fewer than the red vase. The yellow vase has 6 flowers. How many flowers are in the red vase? Show your thinking.

☐ flowers

Step In Carmela bought the book that costs $9 and one other book as a present for a friend. She spent $16 in total.

What was the price of the other book she bought?
How could you figure it out?

I could start at $9, count on $1 to make $10, then add $6 more to make $16. The total of the amount I added is the price of the other book.

What other way could you figure out the price?

Step Up I. Write the two parts and the total for each domino.

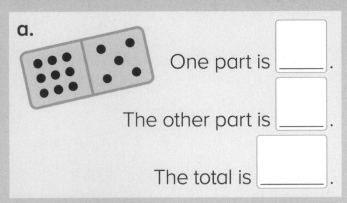

a.

One part is ____.

The other part is ____.

The total is ____.

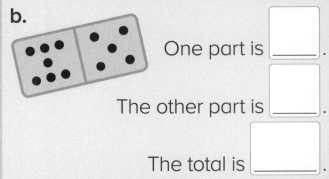

b.

One part is ____.

The other part is ____.

The total is ____.

2. Figure out how many dots are covered on each domino.
Then write two facts to match.

a. **13** dots in total

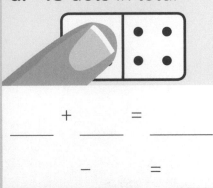

___ + ___ = ___

___ − ___ = ___

b. **12** dots in total

___ + ___ = ___

___ − ___ = ___

c. **15** dots in total

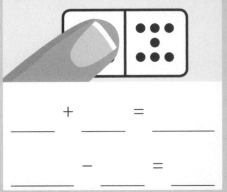

___ + ___ = ___

___ − ___ = ___

3. The circle shows the total. The squares show the parts.
Write the missing numbers, then write the fact family to match.

a.

_____ + _____ = _____

_____ + _____ = _____

_____ − _____ = _____

_____ − _____ = _____

b.

_____ + _____ = _____

_____ + _____ = _____

_____ − _____ = _____

_____ − _____ = _____

c.

_____ + _____ = _____

_____ + _____ = _____

_____ − _____ = _____

_____ − _____ = _____

4. Use the same color to show facts that belong in the same fact family.

4 + 7 = 11	5 + 7 = 12	11 − 4 = 7	12 = 8 + 4
8 + 6 = 14	4 + 8 = 12	12 − 5 = 7	14 − 8 = 6
12 = 7 + 5	14 − 6 = 8	12 − 4 = 8	11 − 7 = 4
11 = 7 + 4	12 − 8 = 4	12 − 7 = 5	14 = 6 + 8

Step Ahead Figure out the number that each symbol represents.
Then write the missing totals.

a.
9 + ⬤ = 13

16 − ▲ = 7

▲ + ⬤ = ☐

b.
◼ + 7 = 11

16 − ◎ = 4

◼ + ◎ = ☐

Think and Solve Brett made a bead belt that started like this.

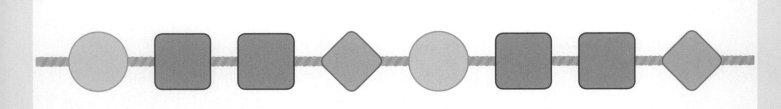

He followed the pattern. He used a total of 40 beads.
How many of each bead did he use?

a.

b.

c.

Words at Work Write about two different **addition** strategies you can use to solve this equation.

$$17 - 8 = ?$$

_____

_____

_____

_____

_____

_____

_____

_____

_____

_____

Ongoing Practice

1. Write **inches**, **feet**, or **yards** to show how you would measure each of these.

a. car

b. kitchen

c. picture frame

d. school building

e. bed

f. shoe

2. Use the same color to show facts that belong in the same fact family.

$15 = 9 + 6$	$13 - 7 = 6$	$11 - 6 = 5$	$13 - 9 = 4$
$5 + 6 = 11$	$15 - 6 = 9$	$4 + 9 = 13$	$15 = 6 + 9$
$13 - 6 = 7$	$6 + 5 = 11$	$15 - 9 = 6$	$6 + 7 = 13$

Preparing for Module 6

Students voted for their favorite fruit. This table shows their votes.

Draw ◯ in the graph below to show each vote.

Our Favorite Fruit

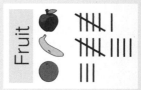

Fruit

© ORIGO Education

Step In

How could you figure out the total cost of buying one adult ticket and one child ticket?

KAYAKING TRIPS
Child $26
Adult $52

You could use a hundred chart. Start at 52. Count down 2 tens and then count across 6 ones.

Hiro thought of another way. He drew this picture to help.

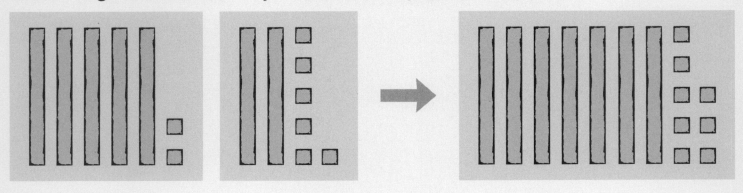

What do you think the shapes represent?

What equations could you write to match the problem?

Step Up

1. Draw simple pictures to show how to group the tens blocks and group the ones blocks. Then complete the sentences.

a.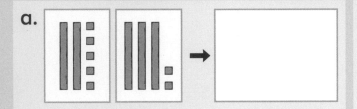

There are _____ tens.

There are _____ ones.

_____ and _____ is _____

b.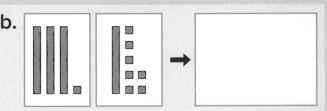

There are _____ tens.

There are _____ ones.

_____ and _____ is _____

2. Add the tens blocks then add the ones blocks. Write the total value of the blocks.

a. 45 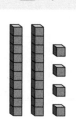 34

There are _____ tens.

There are _____ ones.

_____ and _____ is _____

b. 24 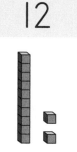 25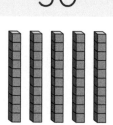

There are _____ tens.

There are _____ ones.

_____ and _____ is _____

c. 12 50

There are _____ tens.

There are _____ ones.

_____ and _____ is _____

3. Complete the equation. Show your thinking.

28 + 41 = [   ]

© ORIGO Education

Step In

Look at this shirt.
What will be the total cost of two shirts?

○ **$20**

How could you figure it out?

20 is the same value as 2 tens.
Double 2 is 4 so double 2 tens
is 4 tens. The total is $40.

How could you figure out the total cost
of two pairs of shorts?

○ **$23**

23 + 23 = ☐
20 + 20 = ☐
3 + 3 = ☐

I could double the tens first.
Double 20 is 40. Then I would
double the ones. Double 3 is
6. So $40 plus $6 is $46.

Step Up

1. Write the missing totals.

a.
if → 2 + 2 = 4
then → 20 + 20 = 40

b.
if → 4 + 4 = ☐
then → 40 + 40 = ☐

c.
if → 5 + 5 = ☐
then → 50 + 50 = ☐

d.
if → 3 + 3 = ☐
then → 30 + 30 = ☐

© ORIGO Education

2. Double the tens, **then** double the ones. Write the total.

a. 12 + 12

Double $\boxed{10}$ is $\boxed{20}$

Double $\boxed{2}$ is $\boxed{4}$

$\boxed{20}$ + $\boxed{4}$ = $\boxed{}$

b. 31 + 31

Double $\boxed{30}$ is $\boxed{}$

Double $\boxed{}$ is $\boxed{}$

$\boxed{}$ + $\boxed{}$ = $\boxed{}$

c. 24 + 24

Double $\boxed{}$ is $\boxed{}$

Double $\boxed{}$ is $\boxed{}$

$\boxed{}$ + $\boxed{}$ = $\boxed{}$

d. 43 + 43

Double $\boxed{}$ is $\boxed{}$

Double $\boxed{}$ is $\boxed{}$

$\boxed{}$ + $\boxed{}$ = $\boxed{}$

3. Write the totals.

a. 14 + 14 = $\boxed{}$

b. 21 + 21 = $\boxed{}$

c. 44 + 44 = $\boxed{}$

d. 33 + 33 = $\boxed{}$

e. 42 + 42 = $\boxed{}$

f. 13 + 13 = $\boxed{}$

Step Ahead

Choose one of the equations from Question 3. Write a doubles story to match.

Computation Practice

★ Complete the equations.
★ Then write each letter above its matching total at the bottom of the page.
   Some letters appear more than once.

13 + 13 = ☐ **p**

29 + 29 = ☐ **t**

18 + 16 = ☐ **g**

11 + 12 = ☐ **m**

23 + 22 = ☐ **n**

16 + 16 = ☐ **l**

16 + 14 = ☐ **r**

41 + 42 = ☐ **c**

21 + 23 = ☐ **i**

24 + 25 = ☐ **h**

25 + 26 = ☐ **e**

45 + 45 = ☐ **s**

30 + 31 = ☐ **a**

☐	☐	☐	☐	☐	☐	,	☐	☐	☐	☐	☐
61	83	61	23	51	32	90	90	26	44	45	51

☐	☐		☐	☐	☐	☐	☐	☐	☐	☐
44	90		90	58	30	61	44	34	49	58

© ORIGO Education

Ongoing Practice

1. a. Draw jumps on this number line to show how you would add 53 and 15.

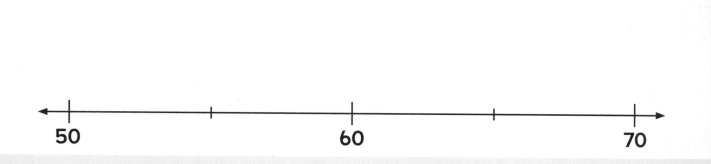

50   60   70

   b. Draw jumps with a different color to show **another way** you could add 53 and 15.

2. Add the tens blocks then the ones blocks. Write the total value of the blocks.

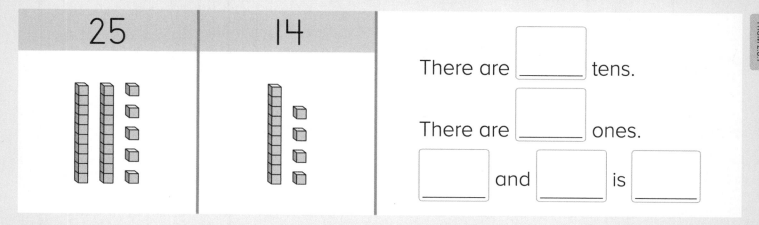

25   14

There are _____ tens.

There are _____ ones.

_____ and _____ is _____

Preparing for Module 7

Draw a line from each number to its position on the number line.

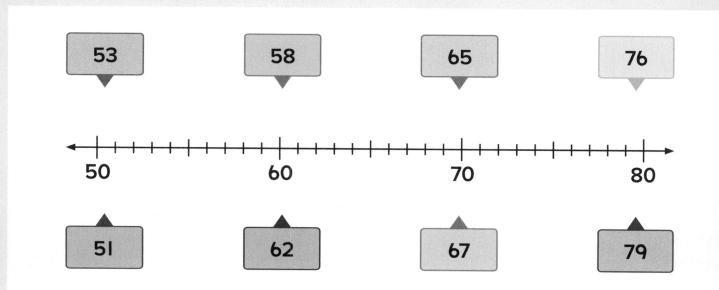

53   58   65   76

50   60   70   80

51   62   67   79

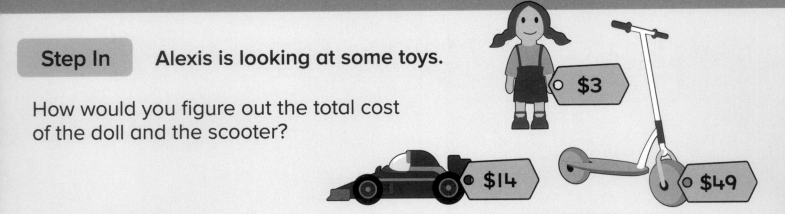

Step In   Alexis is looking at some toys.

How would you figure out the total cost
of the doll and the scooter?

$3

$14

$49

Alexis shows her thinking by drawing this picture.

How can Alexis's picture help you figure out the total cost?

Felix thought about it this way:	Claire thought about it differently:
I see 4 tens and 12 ones. The total must be equal to 40 plus 12, which is 52.	I see 4 tens and 12 ones. I can regroup the 12 ones to make 1 ten and 2 ones. That makes 5 tens and 2 ones so the total is 52.

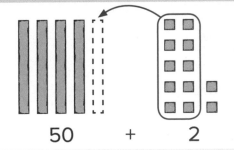

40   +   12   50   +   2

Think about the total cost of the car and the scooter.

Try using Felix's method, then try using Claire's method.
Which do you prefer? Why?

1. Use Felix's method to add. Write the equation to match.

a.

55	17	☐ + ☐ = ☐

b.

43	37	☐ + ☐ = ☐

2. Use Claire's method to add. Write the equation to match.

a.

28	24	☐ + ☐ = ☐

b.

18	58	☐ + ☐ = ☐

Step Ahead

Solve the problem. Draw a picture to show your thinking. Complete the equation.

There are 25 students on one bus and some more students on another bus. There are 51 students in total. How many students are on the other bus?

$$25 + \boxed{} = 51$$

Step In

How could you figure out the total cost of these two books?

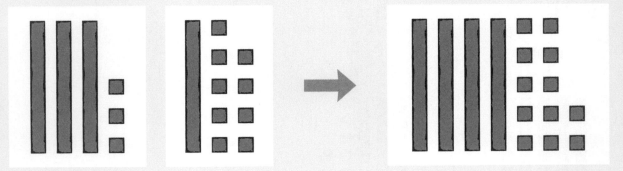

$33 BIKES

$19 BOATS

Oliver drew pictures to help.

How many tens blocks are shown? How many ones?

What methods could you use to figure out the total value of the blocks?

I could add 40 and 12.

Or I could regroup the ones to make another ten.

Step Up

1. Add the tens blocks then add the ones blocks.
   Complete the equation to match.

a.

28   24

$$\boxed{} + \boxed{} = \boxed{}$$

b.

18   58

$$\boxed{} + \boxed{} = \boxed{}$$

2. Complete each equation. Show your thinking.

a.

$37 + 34 = \boxed{}$

b.

$28 + 56 = \boxed{}$

c.

$19 + 45 = \boxed{}$

d.

$37 + 48 = \boxed{}$

3. Complete each equation. You can use blocks or make notes on page 232 to help.

a. $73 + 18 = \boxed{}$

b. $52 + 39 = \boxed{}$

c. $65 + 17 = \boxed{}$

Step Ahead Write digits to complete true equations.

a.

b.

Think and Solve Same shapes weigh the same.
Write the missing value inside each shape.

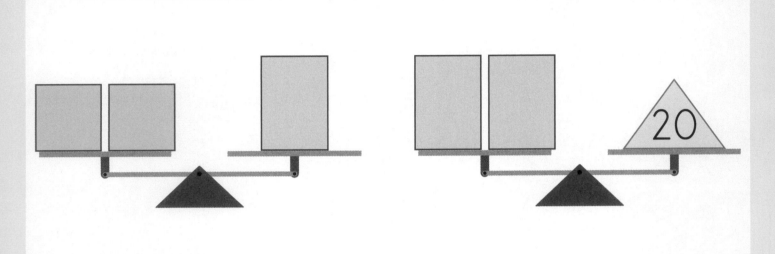

Circle the shape that is the heaviest.

Words at Work Write about how you can use the doubles strategy to figure out this total.

$$43 + 43 = ?$$

Ongoing Practice

1. Figure out each total. Draw jumps to show your thinking.

a.

$$37 + 14 = \boxed{}$$

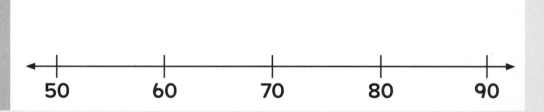

b.

$$59 + 26 = \boxed{}$$

2. Double the tens, **then** double the ones. Write the total.

a. 21 + 21

Double [ ] is [ ]

Double [ ] is [ ]

[ ] + [ ] = [ ]

b. 42 + 42

Double [ ] is [ ]

Double [ ] is [ ]

[ ] + [ ] = [ ]

Preparing for Module 7   Write the missing numbers.

a.
$$7 - 1 = \boxed{}$$

$$17 - 1 = \boxed{}$$

$$27 - 1 = \boxed{}$$

$$37 - 1 = \boxed{}$$

b.
$$15 - 2 = \boxed{}$$

$$25 - 2 = \boxed{}$$

$$35 - 2 = \boxed{}$$

$$45 - 2 = \boxed{}$$

c.
$$17 - 3 = \boxed{}$$

$$27 - 3 = \boxed{}$$

$$37 - 3 = \boxed{}$$

$$47 - 3 = \boxed{}$$

Step In

Emilia needs to fence two sides of her barnyard.

The longer side is **28** yards.
The shorter side is **26** yards.

The wire is sold in different lengths.
What wire should she buy?

20 Yards **50 Yards** **100 Yards**

Both sides are longer than 25 yards, so she'll need more than 50 yards.

Hassun needs **100** yards of wire to fence his barnyard.
He has about **65** yards of wire stored in his barn.

Which single roll of wire should he buy?

65 plus 20 is less than 100 but 65 plus 50 is more than 100, so he should buy the 50-yard roll to have enough.

Step Up

1. Color the label that shows the roll of wire you would buy to fence the two sides.

a.
| 20 yd | 50 yd | 100 yd |

Side A – 8 yards
Side B – 11 yards

b.
| 20 yd | 50 yd | 100 yd |

Side A – 25 yards
Side B – 18 yards

c.
| 20 yd | 50 yd | 100 yd |

Side A – 9 yards
Side B – 17 yards

d.
| 20 yd | 50 yd | 100 yd |

Side A – 37 yards
Side B – 35 yards

2. Read each problem. Then color the label to show your **estimate**.

a. The blue rope is 15 feet long. The red rope is 6 feet longer. About how long is the red rope?

10 ft	20 ft	30 ft

b. Amos joins three pieces of pipe. One is 38 inches long, the second is 25 inches long, and the third is 15 inches long. About how long is the total length?

60 in	70 in	80 in

c. A strip of ribbon is 90 inches long. The strip is cut into two pieces. One piece is 52 inches long. About how long is the other piece?

40 in	50 in	60 in

d. Two hoses that are about the same length are joined together. The total length is 78 feet. About how long is each hose?

30 ft	40 ft	50 ft

3. Estimate each total. Color the cards that have a total **greater than** 80.

a. 38 + 28	**b.** 45 + 47	**c.** 8 + 57	**d.** 27 + 59	**e.** 37 + 25
f. 19 + 73	**g.** 50 + 26	**h.** 39 + 35	**i.** 38 + 41	**j.** 12 + 61

Step Ahead

Dallas joins two of these ribbons together. The total length is about 90 inches. Color the two ribbons that you think she joined.

75 inches

45 inches

16 inches

54 inches

Step In

Imagine you threw three small beanbags onto this target.

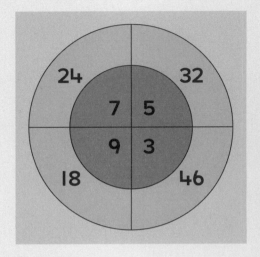

If each beanbag lands on the orange circle, what total scores might you record?

How could you figure out the totals?

I chose 7, 9, and 3.
Then I added in this order,
7 + 3 + 9 because 7 + 3
makes 10 which is easy.

Imagine two beanbags land on pink and one beanbag lands on orange.

How could you figure out the total scores you could record?

I could add friendly pairs of numbers like 18 and 32 first.

Why are 18 and 32 called friendly pairs?

What other numbers make friendly pairs?

Step Up

1. Imagine two beanbags land on **different** yellow parts of this target, and one beanbag lands on a red part. Write equations to show four possible total scores.

$$40 + 10 + 8 =$$

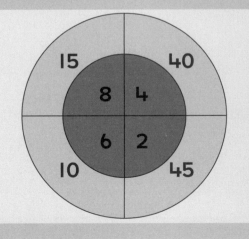

2. Imagine two beanbags land on yellow and one beanbag lands on red. Write equations to show four possible total scores.

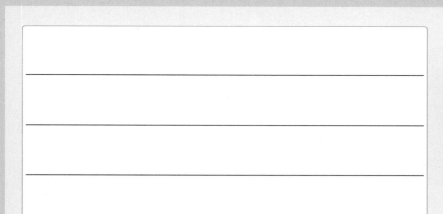
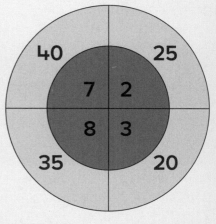

3. Imagine two beanbags land on pink and one beanbag lands on orange. Write equations to show four possible total scores.

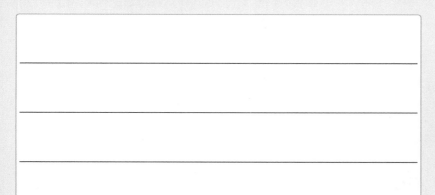
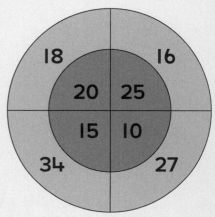

Step Ahead Beatrice threw **three** beanbags onto this target and scored a total of 55. Where did the beanbags land?

Write equations to show three different possible solutions.

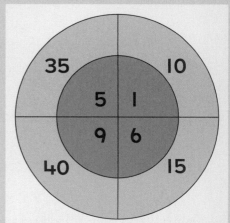

Maintaining concepts and skills

Computation Practice

★ Complete these facts as fast as you can.

start

12 − 9 = ___

14 − 6 = ___

7 − 3 = ___

11 − 5 = ___

10 − 4 = ___

16 − 9 = ___

8 − 2 = ___

15 − 7 = ___

13 − 8 = ___

12 − 5 = ___

9 − 1 = ___

14 − 8 = ___

7 − 5 = ___

11 − 3 = ___

10 − 6 = ___

17 − 9 = ___

6 − 2 = ___

15 − 6 = ___

13 − 7 = ___

5 − 1 = ___

finish

Ongoing Practice

1. Figure out each total. Draw jumps to show your thinking.

a.

38 + 5 = ☐

⟵————————————————————————⟶

b.

65 + 12 = ☐

⟵————————————————————————⟶

2. Add the tens blocks then add ones blocks. Complete the equation to match. Show your thinking.

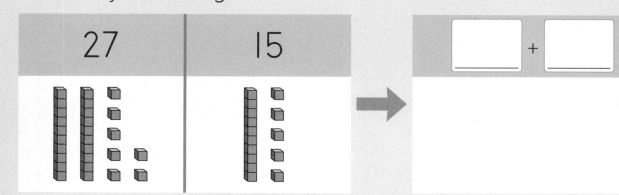

27   15   →   ☐ + ☐ = ☐

Preparing for Module 7

Write the answers. Draw jumps on the number track to help you.

| 1 | 2 | 3 | 4 | 5 | 6 | 7 | 8 | 9 | 10 |

a.

4 − 1 = ☐

b.

6 − 2 = ☐

c.

9 − 2 = ☐

Step In

Do you think that the total cost of these two items is more or less than $100?

How did you decide?

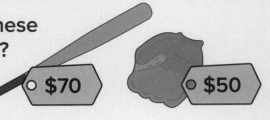

○ $70   ○ $50

Pati shows her thinking by drawing this picture.

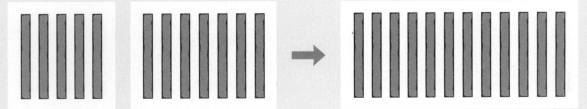

How can Pati's picture help you figure out the total cost?

Tyler thought about it this way:

I see 12 tens. 12 tens is the same value as 120.

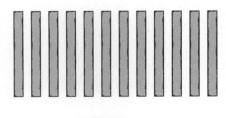

12 tens

Fiona thought about it differently:

I see 12 tens. I can regroup the 12 tens to make 1 hundred and 2 tens. That is 120.

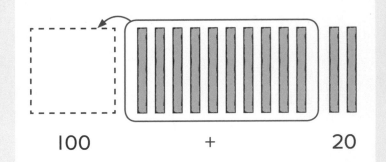

100   +   20

Step Up   1.   Write the missing totals.

a.

if $9 + 4 = 13$

then $90 + 40 = 130$

b.

if $7 + 7 = \underline{}$

then $70 + 70 = \underline{}$

2. Add the blocks and write the total. Show your thinking.

a.

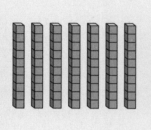 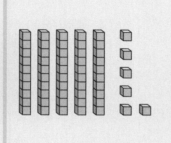

Total = [ ]

b.

Total = [ ]

3. Complete each equation. You can use blocks or make notes on page 232 to help.

a.
$60 + 60 =$ [ ]

b.
$90 + 45 =$ [ ]

c.
$70 + 58 =$ [ ]

d.
$50 + 65 =$ [ ]

e.
$31 + 70 =$ [ ]

f.
$94 + 60 =$ [ ]

Step Ahead

The total value of some blocks is 124.
There are more ones blocks than tens blocks.

Write how many tens blocks and
ones blocks there could be.
Show your thinking.

[ ] tens and [ ] ones.

Step In	Ticket sales for a new movie are shown in this table.

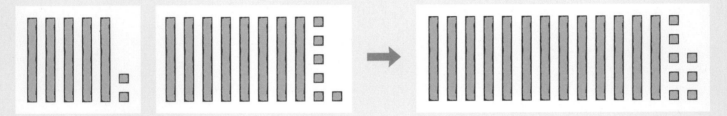

The Sleepy Dragon	
Session	Ticket Sales
Morning	52
Evening	86

What can you tell about the sales?

Do you think that more or fewer than 150 tickets were sold in total? How did you decide?

Ashley drew pictures to help.

How many tens blocks are shown? How many ones?

What methods could you use to figure out the total value of the blocks?

There are 13 tens ... that's 130. Then I could add 130 and 8.

Or I could regroup the tens to make a hundred. Then I could add 100, 30, and 8.

Step Up	I. Add the tens blocks then add the ones blocks. Write an equation to match.

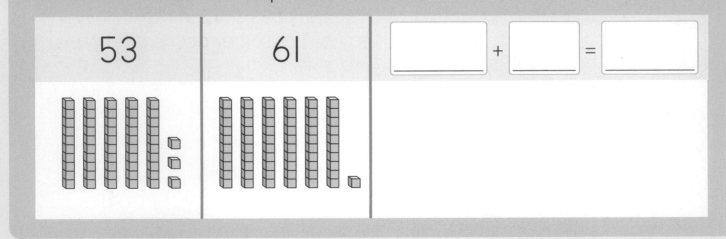

53   61   ☐ + ☐ = ☐

2. Complete each equation. Show your thinking.

a.

75 + 42 = ☐

b.

93 + 34 = ☐

c.

41 + 68 = ☐

3. Complete each equation. You can use blocks or make notes on page 232 to help.

a.
74 + 74 = ☐

b.
91 + 25 = ☐

c.
31 + 73 = ☐

Step Ahead

Grace earned $95 in one month. She put the money into her savings account. She now has $142 in her savings account. How much money was in her account before? Show your thinking.

$ ☐

Think and Solve Look at this number. **50**

Complete these equations to show different ways to make 50.

a. [ ] + [ ] = 50

b. [ ] – [ ] = 50

c. [ ] + [ ] + [ ] = 50

d. [ ] + [ ] + [ ] = 50

Words at Work Choose and write words from the list to complete these sentences. One word is not used.

Word list:
add
regroup
zero
addition
total
ten
equals

a. An equation uses the _____ symbol.

b. You can add three or more numbers in any order

and the _____ will be the same.

c. You can _____ ten ones to make one ten.

d. 406 has four hundreds, _____ tens, and six ones.

e. You can regroup _____ tens to make one hundred.

f. 16 and 4 are a friendly pair of numbers because

they are easy to _____ in your head.

Ongoing Practice

1. Draw dots to help you complete the subtraction fact. Then write a related addition fact.

a.

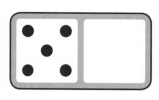

$12 - 5 =$ ☐

$5 +$ ☐ $= 12$

b.

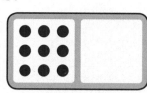

$15 - 9 =$ ☐

$9 +$ ☐ $= 15$

c.

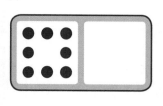

$11 - 8 =$ ☐

$8 +$ ☐ $= 11$

d.

$12 - 3 =$ ☐

$3 +$ ☐ $= 12$

2. Imagine two beanbags land on different purple parts and one beanbag lands on yellow. Write addition equations to show four possible total scores.

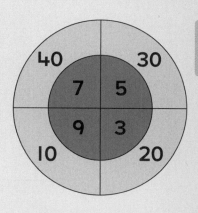

Preparing for Module 7

Figure out how many dots are covered. Then write the matching equations.

a. **9 dots in total**

☐ $+$ ☐ $=$ ☐

☐ $-$ ☐ $=$ ☐

b. **6 dots in total**

☐ $+$ ☐ $=$ ☐

☐ $-$ ☐ $=$ ☐

c. **8 dots in total**

☐ $+$ ☐ $=$ ☐

☐ $-$ ☐ $=$ ☐

Step In

Daniel buys one adult's ticket and one child's ticket.

SKY RAIL

| Adult | $76 |
| Child | $58 |

Do you think that he will pay more or less than $150? How did you decide?

Eva drew pictures to help.

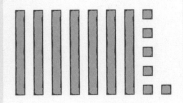  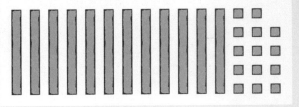

What can you say about the total numbers of tens and ones?

What regrouping could you do to help figure out the total?

Could you figure out the total without regrouping? How?

Step Up

1. Add the tens blocks then add the ones blocks. Write an equation to match.

a.

| 65 | 57 | ☐ + ☐ = ☐ |

b.

| 45 | 76 | ☐ + ☐ = ☐ |

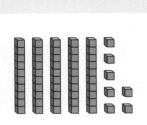   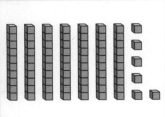

2. Complete each equation. Show your thinking.

a.
$89 + 34 =$ _____

b.
$27 + 86 =$ _____

3. Complete each equation. You can use blocks or make notes on page 232 to help.

a.
$85 + 37 =$ _____

b.
$59 + 59 =$ _____

c.
$43 + 88 =$ _____

4. Solve each problem. Show your thinking.

a. Carmen makes a necklace with 83 red beads and 17 blue beads. How many beads did she use in total?

_____ beads

b. Harvey has 69 toy cars and his brother has 49 toy cars. How many toy cars do they have in total?

_____ toy cars

Step Ahead Write the missing digits to complete true equations.

a. There are 12 tens and 8 ones.

$\boxed{5\ \ } + \boxed{\ \ 3} = \boxed{\ \ 8}$

b. There are 14 tens and 17 ones.

$\boxed{7\ \ } + \boxed{\ \ 9} = \boxed{\ \ \ 7}$

© ORIGO Education

Step In

Camila asked some students to vote for their favorite type of movie. She showed the results with this picture graph.

Favorite Movies   🍿 means I vote

Type of movie	Number of votes
Comedy	🍿 🍿 🍿 🍿 🍿 🍿 🍿 🍿 🍿 🍿 🍿 🍿
Scary	🍿 🍿
Cartoon	🍿 🍿 🍿 🍿 🍿 🍿 🍿 🍿 🍿
Action	🍿 🍿 🍿 🍿 🍿

Number of votes

How many students voted for each type of movie?

What types of movies are more popular than Action?

How many more students voted for Comedy than Scary?

How many fewer students voted for Scary than Cartoon?

How many students voted in total?

Step Up

1. Your teacher will help your class to vote for their favorite type of movie. Record the results in this tally chart.

Type of Movie	Tally	Total
Comedy	卌 ‖	
Cartoon	│	
Action	卌 卌 │	

2. a. Draw  to create a picture graph that shows your results.

Favorite Movies
☁ means 1 vote

Type of movie															
Comedy	0	0	0	0	0	0 0								
Cartoon	0													
Action	0 0	0 0	0 0	0 0	0 0	0 0	0							

Number of votes

3. Use your results to answer each question.

a. What is the least popular type of movie? cartooh

b. How many students voted for Comedy and Action? 7

c. How many students voted in total? 1

d. What is the difference in the number of votes for Action and Cartoon? 12

Step Ahead   Read each of the clues. Then draw ☁ to complete the picture graph.

Clue 1	6 students voted for Cartoon.
Clue 2	2 more students voted for Comedy than Cartoon.
Clue 3	16 students voted in total.

Favorite Movies
☁ means 1 vote

Type of movie													
Action	0	0	0	0 0	0	0 0	0	0	0 0			
Cartoon	0											
Comedy	0	0	0 0	0	0 0	0						

Number of votes

Computation Practice   **What can you sometimes see in the sky at night?**

★ Write all the totals.
★ Then color all the parts that show each total in the puzzle below.

27 + 12 = **39**	11 + 22 = **35**	31 + 11 = **45**
35 + 11 = **46**	24 + 12 = **31**	17 + 12 = **35**
19 + 22 =	18 + 20 =	29 + 11 =
13 + 21 =	39 + 11 =	25 + 22 =

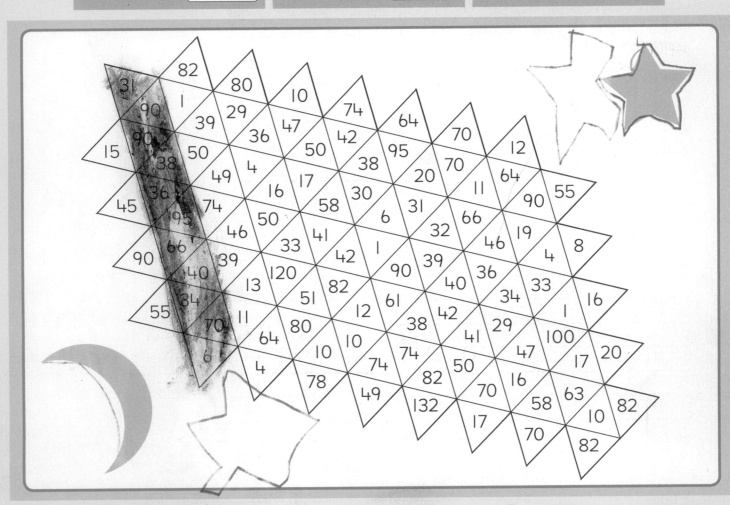

ORIGO Stepping Stones · Grade 2 · 6.10

Ongoing Practice

1. Solve each problem. Show your thinking.

FROM 2.5.11

a. 15 children are playing at the park. 6 are on the slide and the rest are playing ball. How many children are playing ball?

☐ children

b. Dad baked 12 fruit muffins. He took 8 to work. How many muffins did he leave at home?

☐ muffins

2. Complete the equation. Show your thinking.

FROM 2.6.8

$67 + 51 = $ ☐

Preparing for Module 7

Write each answer. Draw jumps above the number track to show your thinking. Make your first jump to 10.

a.

$12 - 9 = $ ☐

1	2	3	4	5	6	7	8	9	10	11	12	13	14	15

b.

$15 - 6 = $ ☐

1	2	3	4	5	6	7	8	9	10	11	12	13	14	15

Step In   Look at this graph.

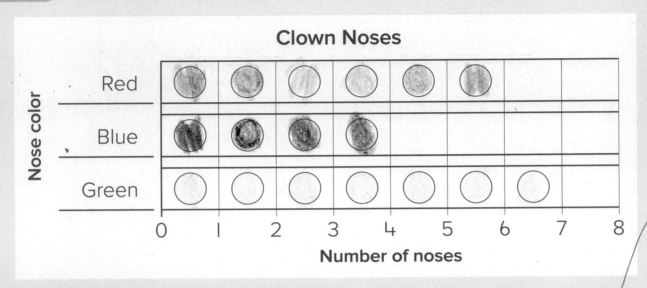

Clown Noses

How many clown noses are there in each color?

How can you figure out the number of different clown noses without counting?

How many more noses are red than blue? How do you know? How many fewer noses are blue than green?

> You don't need to draw clown noses. You could just color spaces beside each color name.

Step Up   I.   Use colors to show balls that are the same.

2. Color this graph to show the number of each type of ball in Question 1.

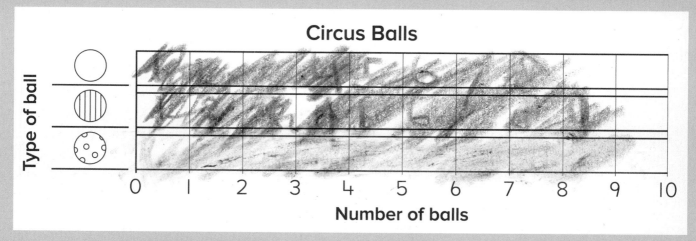

3. Use the graph above to answer these questions.

a. How many balls had spots?

 8

b. How many more balls had spots than stripes?

 8

c. How many fewer balls had stripes than no pattern?

 9

d. How many balls are there in total?

 24

Step Ahead

Read each clue. Then write **red**, **blue**, and **green** to complete the graph.

Clue 1 The fewest number of clowns wore blue noses.
Clue 2 More clowns wore green noses than red noses.

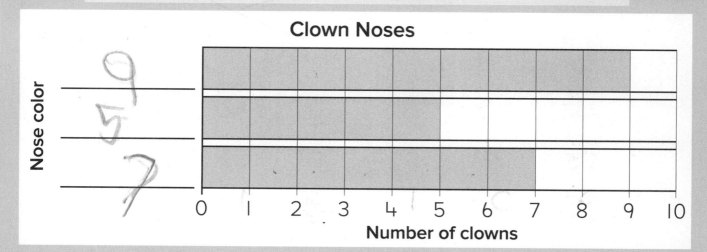

Step In

Look at these flowering plants.

How would you describe the height of each plant?

What type of graph could you use to compare the heights?

Why did you choose that type of graph?

Where would you write the numbers that show the height of each plant?

Sunflower   Daffodil   Daisy

Step Up

1. Write the height of each plant.

a.
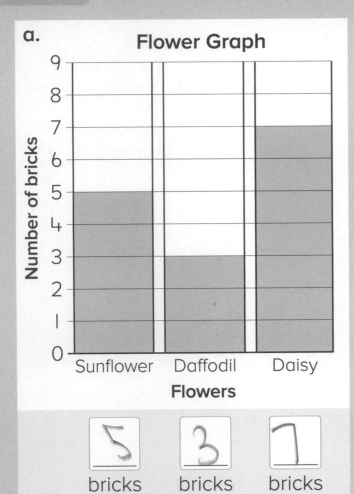

5	3	7
bricks	bricks	bricks

b.
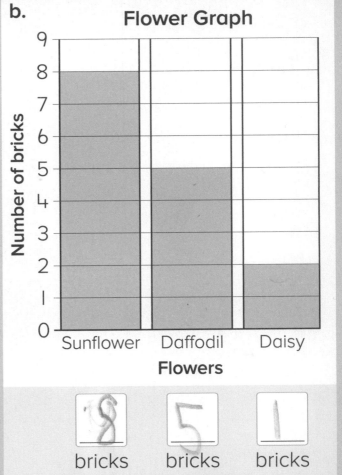

8	5	1
bricks	bricks	bricks

2. Color the bar graph to match the plant heights.

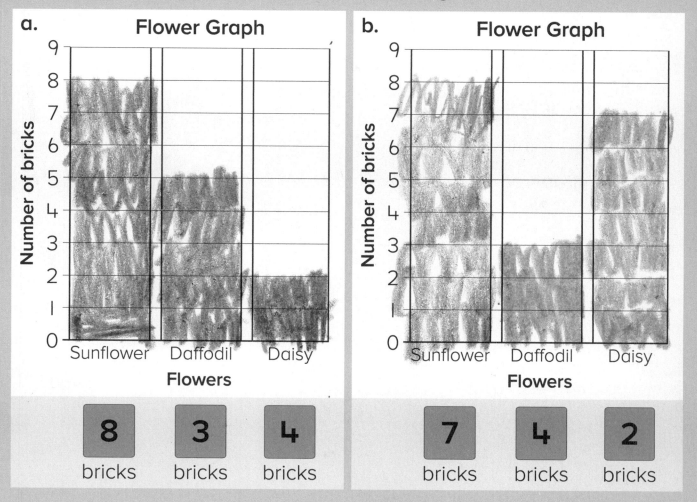

a. Flower Graph

8	3	4
bricks	bricks	bricks

b. Flower Graph

7	4	2
bricks	bricks	bricks

Step Ahead

Color this bar graph to match the clue. Then write the numbers.

Clue

The Marigold is shorter than the Rose but taller than the Violet.

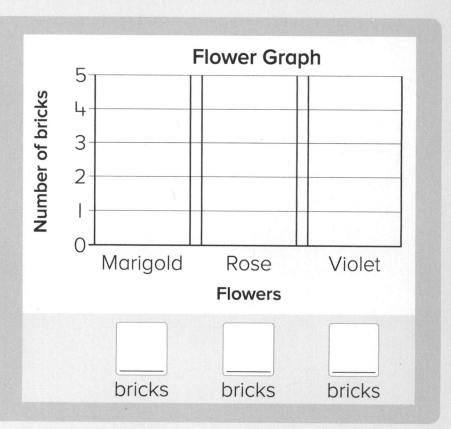

Flower Graph

bricks	bricks	bricks

Think and Solve

The picture on the left below is a magic L. The total of the numbers in each straight line is the same. The magic total is 14.

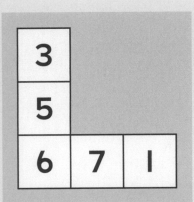

Use these numbers to make a magic L with a magic total of 20.

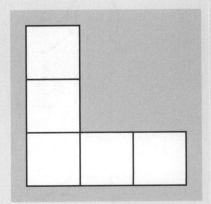

Words at Work

Write about how you could find out the most popular type of fruit in your class. Describe how you could record the data. You can use words from the list to help.

data
graph
tally mark
table
popular
vote

© ORIGO Education

Ongoing Practice

1. The ● shows the total. The ■ show the parts. Write the missing part and the fact family.

a.

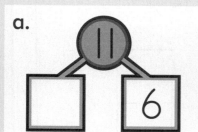

☐ + ☐ = ☐   ☐ − ☐ = ☐

☐ + ☐ = ☐   ☐ − ☐ = ☐

b.

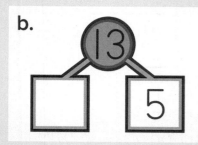

☐ + ☐ = ☐   ☐ − ☐ = ☐

☐ + ☐ = ☐   ☐ − ☐ = ☐

2. Color the graph below to show the number of each type of ball.

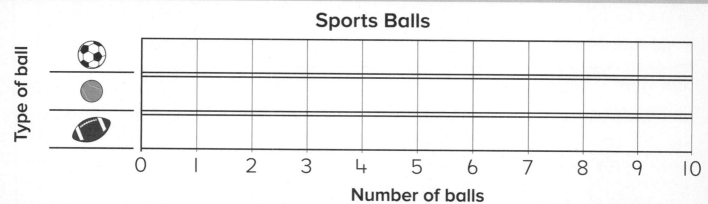

Sports Balls

Type of ball

Number of balls

0 1 2 3 4 5 6 7 8 9 10

Preparing for Module 7

Draw two hexagons that look different.

STUDENT GLOSSARY

3D object

A **three-dimensional (3D) object** has flat surfaces (e.g. a cube), curved surfaces (e.g. a sphere), or flat and curved surfaces (e.g. a cylinder or a cone).

A **polyhedron** is any closed 3D object that has four or more flat surfaces.

A **pyramid** is a polyhedron that has any polygon for a base. All the other surfaces joined to the base are triangles that meet at a point.

Addition

Part + Part = Total
2 + 3 = 5

Addition is finding the total when two or more parts are known. When adding, another word for total is **sum**.

Capacity

Capacity tells the amount a container can hold. For example, a cup **holds less** than a juice bottle.

A **liter** is a unit of capacity.
A **pint** is a unit of capacity.
A **quart** is a unit of capacity.

Common Fraction

Fractions describe equal parts of one whole.

one-half

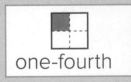

one-fourth

Even and odd numbers

Even numbers are whole numbers with 0, 2, 4, 6, or 8 in the ones place.
Odd numbers are whole numbers with 1, 3, 5, 7, or 9 in the ones place.

Fact family

An addition **fact family** includes an addition fact, its turnaround fact, and the two related subtraction facts.

$$4 + 2 = 6$$
$$2 + 4 = 6$$
$$6 - 4 = 2$$
$$6 - 2 = 4$$

STUDENT GLOSSARY

Graph

Different types of **graphs** can show data.

Vertical bar graph

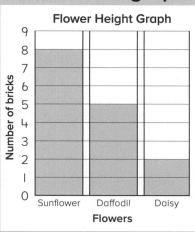

Horizontal bar graph

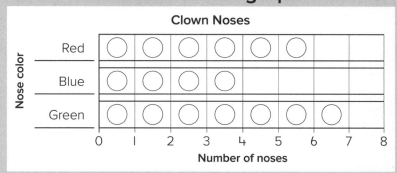

Line plot

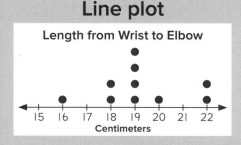

Picture graph

Hundred chart

A **hundred chart** makes it easy to see patterns with two-digit numbers.

Length

Length tells how long something is.

A **centimeter** is a unit of length. The short way to write centimeter is **cm**.

The **foot** is a unit of length. There are 3 feet in one yard. The short way to write foot is **ft**.

The **inch** is a unit of length. There are 12 inches in one foot. The short way to write inch is **in**.

A **meter** is a unit of length. The short way to write meter is **m**.

A **yard** is a unit of length. The short way to write yard is **yd**.

Mass

Mass tells the amount something weighs.
For example, a cat **weighs more** than a mouse.

A **kilogram** is a unit of mass. The short way to write kilogram is **kg**.

A **pound** is a unit of mass. The short way to write pound is **lb**.

Mental computation strategies for addition

Strategies you can use to figure out a mathematical problem in your head.

Count-on   *See* 3 + 8   *think* 8 + 1 + 1 + 1
                 See 58 + 24   *think* 58 + 10 + 10 + 4

Doubles   *See* 7 + 7   *think* double 7
                 See 25 + 26   *think* double 25 plus 1 more
                 See 35 + 37   *think* double 35 plus 2 more

Make-ten   *See* 9 + 4   *think* 9 + 1 + 3
                 See 38 + 14   *think* 38 + 2 + 12

Place value   *See* 32 + 27   *think* 32 + 20 + 7

Mental computation strategies for subtraction

Strategies you can use to figure out a mathematical problem in your head.

Count-back   *See* 9 − 2   *think* 9 − 1 − 1
                 See 26 − 20   *think* 26 − 10 − 10

Think addition   *See* 17 − 9   *think* 9 + 8 = 17 so 17 − 9 = 8

Multiplication

Multiplication is used to find the total number of objects in an array, or in a number of equal groups.

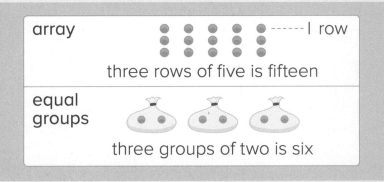

array ------ 1 row

three rows of five is fifteen

equal groups

three groups of two is six

Number facts

Addition facts are equations that add two one-digit numbers.
For example: $2 + 3 = 5$ or $3 = 1 + 2$

Subtraction facts are subtraction equations related
to the addition facts above. For example: $5 - 2 = 3$ or $3 - 2 = 1$

Number line

A **number line** shows the position
of a number. The number line can
be used to show addition and subtraction.

Polygon

A **polygon** is any closed 2D shape
that has three or more straight sides
(e.g. triangle, quadrilateral, pentagon, and hexagon).

Subtraction

Subtraction is finding a part when
the total and one part are known.

Total − Part = Part
$5 - 2 = 3$
Part + __ = Total
$2 + __ = 5$

Turnaround fact

Each addition fact has a related **turnaround fact**. (This is also known as the
Commutative Property.) For example: $2 + 7 = 9$ and $7 + 2 = 9$

TEACHER INDEX

TEACHER INDEX

TEACHER INDEX